First Star
The Blue-Pillowed Sky
A Shiny Golden Path
Rainbow Bridge
Slide Down the Sky
From Sea to Shining Sea
Time for Dreams
Across the World
Over the Moon
Sound of the Sea
Promises to Keep

Night is a beautiful thing,
One big black ball
As the clouds push it around.
Sometimes I think I am being rolled
    over by it.
Sometimes I think it's smiling at me.
The moon is the nose.
The stars are the mouth.
And it is drinking the Milky Way.
Sometimes I dream that it will
    swallow me.
Night is the time for dreams,
Not day dreams but night dreams.

—Sam Gilford, Age 8

# Time for Dreams

An anthology
compiled and edited by

**Zena Sutherland** and **Marilyn F. Cunningham**

**Program Authors**

Carl Bereiter
Marlene Scardamalia
Ann Brown
Valerie Anderson
Joseph Campione
Walter Kintsch

Open Court
La Salle, Illinois

**President and Publisher**
M. Blouke Carus

**Education Director**
Carl Bereiter

**Project Coordination**
Marsha Roit

**Project Planning and Implementation**
Thomas G. Anderson,
Commonwealth Strategies, Inc.

**Senior Editor**
Marilyn F. Cunningham

**Permissions**
Diane Sikora

**Art Direction**
Todd Sanders

**Cover Design**
James Buddenbaum

OPEN COURT and ✿ are registered in the
U.S. Patent and Trademark Office.

Printed in the United States of America

ISBN 0-8126-3115-3

# Acknowledgments

Grateful acknowledgment is given to the following publishers and copyright owners for permission granted to reprint selections from their publications. All possible care has been taken to trace ownership and secure permission for each selection included.

Mary D. Bailey, for "The Gravestone Snake"; © 1986 by Mary D. Bailey.

Byrd Baylor, for "And It Is Still That Way" by Byrd Baylor, "Coyote and the Money Tree" by Tina Naiche, and "The Tricky Coyote" by William Penn, from *And It Is Still That Way* by Byrd Baylor; copyright © 1976 by Byrd Baylor.

Carnival Enterprises, for an adaptation of *Angel Child, Dragon Child* by Michele Maria Surat; text copyright © 1983 by Carnival Press, Inc.

Crown Publishers, Inc., for "The Planets," from *The Long View into Space* by Seymour Simon; copyright © 1979 by Seymour Simon.

Delacorte Press/Seymour Lawrence and William Jay Smith, for "The Toaster," excerpted from the book *Laughing Time: Nonsense Poems* by William Jay Smith, published by Delacorte Press 1980; copyright © 1953, 1955, 1956, 1957, 1959, 1968, 1974, 1977, 1980 by William Jay Smith.

Dial Books for Young Readers, for an adaptation of *Mandy's Grandmother* by Liesel Moak Skorpen; text copyright © 1975 by Liesel Moak Skorpen.

Dillon Press, Inc., for an excerpt from *A Gift for Tía Rosa* by Karen T. Taha; © 1986 by Dillon Press, Inc.

E. P. Dutton, a division of NAL Penguin Inc.: for an adaptation of *The Magic Wings* by Diane Wolkstein, text copyright © 1983 by Diane Wolkstein; and for excerpts from *When I Was Young in the Mountains* by Cynthia Rylant, illustrated by Diane Goode, text copyright © 1982 by Cynthia Rylant, illustrations copyright © 1982 by Diane Goode.

E. P. Dutton, a division of NAL Penguin Inc., and Methuen & Co. Ltd., for excerpts from *Winnie-the-Pooh* by A. A. Milne, illustrated by Ernest H. Shepard; copyright 1926 by E. P. Dutton, renewed 1954 by A. A. Milne.

Doris Holmes Eyges, for "Rhyme of Rain" by John Holmes, from *Fair Warning* by John Homes; copyright 1939 by Henry Holt and Company, Inc., copyright renewed by Doris Holmes Eyges, 1966.

A. W. Fleming, for "Who's In?" by Elizabeth Fleming.

Greenwillow Books, a division of William Morrow & Company, for "Play," from *Country Pie* by Frank Asch; text copyright © 1979 by Frank Asch.

# Illustration

Enrico Arno (22, 114), Jim Arnosky (29, 30, 31, 32, 92, 93, 94), Melanie Arwin (148, 149, 150), Joseph Cellini (69), David Cunningham (168), Dee deRose (151, 153, 155, 156, 157), Bert Dodson (95, 96, 98, 100), David Frampton (102), Larry Frederick (48, 49, 50, 183, 184, 186), Imero Gobatto (71), Diane Goode (9, 10, 11), Friso Henstra (8, 91), Lee Hill (42-43, 44-45), Ronald Himler (111), Trina Schart Hyman (14, 16, 20, 33, 35, 37, 39, 40), Bill Jacobson (132), Robin Jacques (82), Pamela Johnson (23, 24-25), Laurie Jordon (167), Carl Koch (73, 74-75, 76-77), Joe Lasker (62, 63, 65, 66), Janet LaSalle (78-79, 142), Laura Leidecker (47, 187, 188-189), Leo Lionni (2-3, 4-5, 6), Diana Magnuson (135, 136, 137, 138, 139, 140), Les Morrill (131), Robert Andrew Parker (161, 163, 165), Rodney Pate (7), Cathy Pavia (158-159), Betty Raskin (12, 17, 19, 21, 177-181), Deborah Kogan Ray (83, 84, 86), Dick Sakahara (cover), Steve Schindler (28), Ernest H. Shepard (117, 119, 121, 124, 125), Shel Silverstein (116), Dick Smolinski (103, 104, 106, 108, 109), Susanna Spann (53, 55, 56-57), Krystyna Stasiak (59, 61), Arvis Stewart (89), Lorna Tormei (166), Bob Totten (144, 146).

# Photography

Art Resource (112), Beth Bergman (127), Les Bottin (178, 180), Early New England Rubbings by Edmund Vincent Gillen, Jr., 1981 ed. Dover (98, 99), Carl Frank (26), Marilyn Gartman Agency (80, 181), Jet Propulsion Lab, California Institute of Technology, NASA, California (169, 170, 171, 172, 173, 174), Dan Morrill (88, 182), Mount Wilson and Los Campanos Observatories, Carnegie Institute of Washington (168), Lauren Rogerts Museum of Art (127), Washoe Science Year. The World Book Science Annual © 1973 Field Enterprise Educational Corp. By permission of World Book, Inc. (51), Wide World Photos, Inc. (176), Yerkes Observatory (175).

# Contents

## Unit One    Imagination

## Unit Two    Misunderstandings

# Unit Three    New Ways of Seeing

# Unit Four    Challenges

# Unit Five    Changes

# Unit One
## Imagination

# Frederick

LEO LIONNI

All along the meadow where the cows grazed and the horses
ran, there was an old stone wall.

In that wall, not far from the barn and the granary, a
chatty family of field mice had their home.

But the farmers had moved away, the barn was
abandoned, and the granary stood empty. And since winter
was not far off, the little mice began to gather
corn and nuts and wheat and straw. They
all worked day and night.

All—except Frederick.

"Frederick, why don't you
work?" they asked.

"I *do* work," said Frederick. "I gather sun rays for the cold, dark winter days."

And when they saw Frederick sitting there, staring at the meadow, they said, "And now, Frederick?"

"I gather colors," answered Frederick simply, "for winter is gray."

And once Frederick seemed half asleep. "Are you dreaming, Frederick?" they asked reproachfully.

But Frederick said, "Oh no, I am gathering words. For the winter days are long and many, and we'll run out of things to say."

The winter days came, and when the first snow fell the five little field mice took to their hideout in the stones.

In the beginning there was lots to eat, and the mice told stories of foolish foxes and silly cats. They were a happy family.

But little by little they had nibbled up most of the nuts and berries, the straw was gone, and the corn was only a memory.

It was cold in the wall and no one felt like chatting.

Then they remembered what Frederick had said about sun rays and colors and words.

"What about *your* supplies, Frederick?" they asked.

"Close your eyes," said Frederick, as he climbed on a big stone. "Now I send you the rays of the sun. Do you feel how their golden glow . . . ?"

And as Frederick spoke of the sun, the four little mice began to feel warmer. Was it Frederick's voice? Was it magic?

"And how about the colors, Frederick?" they asked anxiously.

"Close your eyes again," Frederick said. And when he told them of the blue periwinkles, the red poppies in the yellow wheat, and the green leaves of the berry bush, they saw the colors as clearly as if they had been painted in their minds.

"And the words, Frederick?"

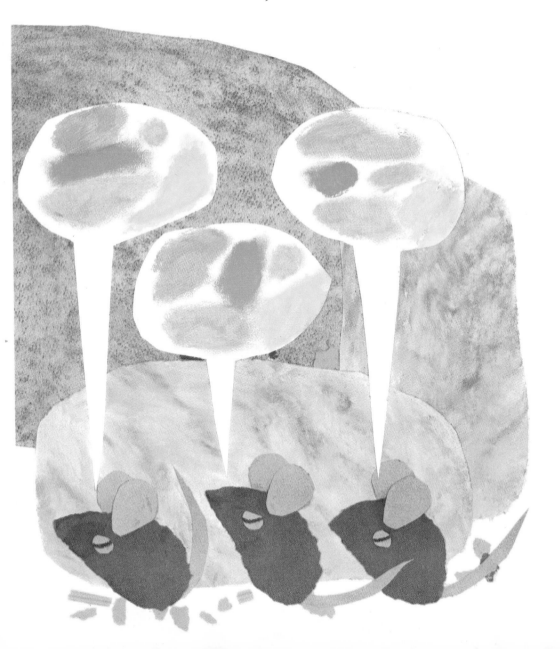

Frederick cleared his throat, waited a moment, and then, as if from a stage, he said:

"*Who scatters snowflakes? Who melts the ice?*
*Who spoils the weather? Who makes it nice?*
*Who grows the four-leaf clovers in June?*
*Who dims the daylight? Who lights the moon?*

*Four little field mice who live in the sky.*
*Four little field mice . . . like you and I.*

*One is the Springmouse who turns on the showers.*
*Then comes the Summer who paints in the flowers.*
*The Fallmouse is next with walnuts and wheat.*
*And Winter is last . . . with little cold feet.*

*Aren't we lucky the seasons are four?*
*Think of a year with one less . . . or one more!*"

When Frederick had finished, they all applauded. "But Frederick," they said, "you are a poet!"

Frederick blushed, took a bow, and said shyly, "I know it."

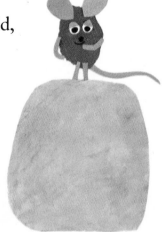

# Things

ELOISE GREENFIELD

Went to the corner
Walked in the store
Bought me some candy
Ain't got it no more
Ain't got it no more

Went to the beach
Played on the shore
Built me a sandhouse
Ain't got it no more
Ain't got it no more

Went to the kitchen
Lay down on the floor
Made me a poem
Still got it
Still got it

7

# The Boy Who Cried Wolf

AESOP

Once there was a young shepherd boy who tended his sheep on a hillside near a dark forest. It was a lonely job, and one day he thought of a way to get a little company and some excitement. He rushed down the hill toward the village shouting, "A wolf, a wolf!"

The villagers heard the boy and thought a wolf was eating his sheep, so they stopped their work and ran to help him. Some of them stayed on the hillside for quite some time, even when they saw that there was no wolf. This pleased the shepherd boy so much that a few days later he tried the same trick, and again the villagers came to his aid.

But then, on the very next day, a wolf really did come out of the forest and begin to chase the sheep. "Wolf, wolf!" cried the boy, louder than ever. This time the villagers, who had been fooled twice before, thought the boy was again playing a trick, and no one came to help.

The wolf ate many of the boy's sheep, and when the boy complained, the wise people of the village said, "A liar will not be believed even when he speaks the truth."

# When I Was Young in the Mountains

CYNTHIA RYLANT

When I was young in the mountains, Grandfather came home in the evening covered with the black dust of a coal mine. Only his lips were clean, and he used them to kiss the top of my head.

When I was young in the mountains, Grandmother spread the table with hot corn bread, pinto beans, and fried okra.

When I was young in the mountains, we walked across the cow pasture and through the woods, carrying our towels. The swimming hole was dark and muddy, and we sometimes saw snakes, but we jumped in anyway.

On our way home, we stopped at Mr. Crawford's for a mound of white butter. Mr. Crawford and Mrs. Crawford looked alike and always smelled of sweet milk.

When I was young in the mountains, we pumped pails of water from the well at the bottom of the hill and heated the water to fill round tin tubs for our baths. Afterward we stood in front of the old black stove, shivering and giggling, while Grandmother heated cocoa on top.

When I was young in the mountains, we listened to frogs sing at dusk and awoke to cowbells outside our windows. Sometimes a black snake came into the yard, and my Grandmother would threaten it with a hoe. If it did not leave, she used the hoe to kill it. Four of us once draped a very long snake, dead of course, across our necks for a photograph.

When I was young in the mountains, we sat on the porch swing in the evenings, and Grandfather sharpened my pencils with his pocketknife. Grandmother sometimes shelled beans and sometimes braided my hair. The dogs lay around us, and the stars sparkled in the sky. A bobwhite whistled in the forest. *Bob-bob-bobwhite!*

When I was young in the mountains, I never wanted to go to the ocean, and I never wanted to go to the desert. I never wanted to go anywhere else in the world, for I was in the mountains. And that was always enough.

# Snow White and the Seven Dwarfs

JACOB and WILHELM GRIMM

## [ PART 1 ]

Once upon a time a queen sat sewing by a window with an ebony frame. It was the middle of winter, and flakes of snow were falling from the sky like feathers. As the queen sat sewing and watching the snow, she pricked her finger with her needle, and three drops of blood fell onto the window ledge. The crimson color on the white snow looked so beautiful that the queen said to herself, "Oh, if only I had a child with skin as white as snow, with lips as red as blood, and with hair as black as the wood of this ebony frame!"

Some time later the queen gave birth to a little daughter with skin as white as snow, with lips as red as blood, and with hair as black as ebony. She named the child Snow White. Soon after the child was born, the young queen died.

A year later the king took another wife. She was beautiful but so proud that she could not bear to think that anyone might be more beautiful than she. The new queen had a magic mirror, and whenever she looked at herself in it, she asked,

*"Mirror, Mirror, on the wall,*
*Who is the fairest one of all?"*
And always the mirror replied,
*"You, O Queen, are the fairest in the land."*
Then the queen was satisfied, for she knew the mirror always told the truth.

As time passed, the little child named Snow White grew more and more beautiful until at last she was more beautiful than the queen herself. One day when the queen asked her mirror,
*"Mirror, Mirror, on the wall,*
*Who is the fairest one of all?"*
the mirror answered,
*"You, O Queen, are the fairest here,*
*But Snow White is fairest in the land."*
The queen gasped and turned green with envy. From that hour, she burned with hatred whenever she saw Snow White. Envy and pride grew like weeds in her heart. At last, she called a hunter and said, "Get that child out of my sight. Take her into the forest and kill her. Bring back her heart as proof."

The hunter obeyed and led the child deep into the forest. Snow White began to cry. "Dear hunter," she begged, "do not kill me. I'll run away into the woods and never come back."

The hunter took pity on her and said, "Run away then, poor child!" He thought the wild beasts would probably kill

Snow White. He had not wanted to kill her, so he felt that a great weight had been lifted from his heart.

As he returned to the castle, the hunter came upon a wild pig, which he killed. He removed the pig's heart and brought it back to the queen, who was happy at last to believe Snow White was dead.

As for poor Snow White, she was now all alone in the great dark forest. She felt frightened and did not know what to do. She began to run—over sharp stones and through thorn bushes. Wild animals passed close by her but did her no harm.

Snow White ran as long as her legs would carry her. Then, just as evening came, she saw a little house and went into it to rest. Everything in the house was very small. There was a little round table covered with a white cloth and set with seven little plates. There were also seven little spoons, knives, forks, and cups. Up against the walls stood seven little beds with sheets as white as snow.

Snow White was hungry and thirsty, so she ate a mouthful from each plate and drank a sip from every cup, because she did not want to eat all of anyone's meal. Then she grew sleepy, so she lay down first on one bed and then on another. She could not make herself comfortable, however, for each bed was either too long or too short. Luckily the seventh bed was just right, so she stayed there, said her prayers, and fell asleep.

When it was quite dark, the owners of the little house came home. They were seven dwarfs who mined for silver and gold among the mountains. As soon as they lighted their seven candles, they saw that someone had been there.

The first asked, "Who has been sitting in my chair?"

The second asked, "Who has been eating off my plate?"

The third asked, "Who has taken a bite of my bread?"

The fourth asked, "Who has been touching my spoon?"

The fifth asked, "Who has been using my fork?"

The sixth asked, "Who has been cutting with my knife?"

The seventh asked, "Who has been drinking out of my cup?"

Then the first dwarf looked around and asked, "Who has been lying in my little bed?"

The others came running, and each called out, "Someone has been lying in my bed, too."

But the seventh, when he looked at his bed, saw Snow White there, sound asleep. He called the others, who flocked around with cries of surprise. They fetched their seven candles and cast the light on Snow White. "What a lovely child!" they cried.

The seven dwarfs were so pleased that they did not waken Snow White but let her sleep on in the little bed. The seventh dwarf slept with the others in turn, an hour with each, and so the night passed.

When morning came, Snow White woke up and was frightened when she saw the seven dwarfs, but they were very friendly to her.

"What is your name?" they asked.

"Snow White," she answered.

"How did you find your way to our house?" the dwarfs asked.

Snow White told them how her stepmother had tried to kill her, how the hunter had spared her life, and how she had run all day until at last she had found their little house.

Then the dwarfs said, "If you will keep house for us, you may stay here with us, and we will take care of you."

"Gladly," said Snow White. And so it was agreed.

## [ PART 2 ]

When the good dwarfs left for the mine in the morning, they warned Snow White, "Beware of your wicked stepmother. She may soon find out that you are here. Don't let anyone into the house."

The queen, back at the castle, had no doubt that she was again the most beautiful woman in the land. She walked up to her mirror and asked,

*"Mirror, Mirror, on the wall,*
*Who is the fairest one of all?"*
The mirror replied,
*"Past seven hills, I tell you true,*
*Lives Snow White, fairer far than you."*
The queen shook with rage. Snow White was still alive! But not for long! "Snow White shall die," she cried, "if it costs my own life!"

Then she went to a secret and lonely room where no one ever came. She stayed there for hours, preparing a poisoned apple. It was so red and ripe and rosy that anyone who saw it would long for it. But a single bite would bring instant death to anyone who tasted it.

When the apple was ready, the queen painted her face and dressed herself as an old peasant woman. She traveled over the seven hills to the home of the dwarfs. There she knocked on the door and cried out, "Apples to sell! Good ripe apples to sell!"

Snow White put her head out of the window and said, "I cannot open the door to anybody. The dwarfs have forbidden me to do so."

"Very well," replied the peasant woman. "I only want to get rid of my apples. Here, try this one!"

"I dare not take it," said Snow White.

"Are you afraid of being poisoned?" said the old woman. "Look here, let me cut this apple in two. You eat one side, and I will eat the other."

Now the fruit was so cleverly treated that only one side of it was poisoned. Snow White longed for the pretty apple, and when she saw the old woman eating, she could not resist. She stretched out her hand and took the poisoned half. Hardly had she tasted the apple when she fell to the floor as if dead.

"As white as snow, as red as blood, and as black as

ebony. There's an end to your beauty."

The queen laughed loudly and watched Snow White for a moment. Then she dashed away.

When she got back to the castle the queen asked the mirror,

*"Mirror, Mirror, on the wall,*
*Who is the fairest of us all?"*

The mirror at last replied,

*"You are now the fairest of them all."*

When the seven dwarfs came home that evening, they found Snow White lying on the floor. They tried to waken her, but she did not breathe.

They lifted Snow White gently to a bed, and all seven of them sat around her and wept for three days and three nights. They knew they should bury her, but they could not bear to hide her away in the cold, black earth. They built a clear glass case, laid her in it, and wrote her name on it in golden letters. Then they carried the case up to the mountain near their house, where one of them could always stay by it to watch over Snow White. But there was little need to guard the case, for even the birds and wild animals came and mourned for their friend.

Years passed. Snow White lay unchanged in her glass case, looking as though she were asleep. Her skin was still as white as snow, her lips as red as blood, and her hair as black as ebony.

Then one day a prince came to the forest and stopped
for the night at the dwarfs' house. He saw the glass case
with the beautiful Snow White in it. Then he said to the
dwarfs, "Let me have the glass case. I will pay you whatever
you want."

But the dwarfs answered, "We would not part with it
for all the gold in the world."

At this the prince said, "Then give it to me as a gift, for
I cannot live without seeing Snow White. Though she is
dead, I will prize and honor her forever."

At last the good dwarfs took pity on the prince and
gave him the glass case. The prince lifted it up, but as he did
so, a tiny piece of the poisoned apple was shaken from
Snow White's throat. Immediately she opened her eyes and
sat up, alive once more. "Where am I?" she asked.

The prince answered, "You are safe with me." Then he told her all that had happened and said, "I love you more than anything else in the world. Come with me to my father's castle and be my wife."

Snow White was well pleased when she heard these words. She went with the prince, and everything was prepared for their wedding.

The wicked queen was invited to the feast. She dressed herself in her richest clothes and stood in front of the mirror saying,

*"Mirror, Mirror, on the wall,*
*Who is the fairest one of all?"*

The mirror answered,

*"O lovely Queen, I tell you true.*
*The bride is fairer far than you."*

The evil-hearted woman could hardly believe her ears. But curiosity would not allow her to rest. She went to the wedding to see who that young queen could be, who was the most beautiful in all the world. When she came and found that it was Snow White alive again, her fear and rage were so great that she fell down dead. No one was sorry, and the prince and Snow White lived happily ever after.

# The Deer

AESOP

One time a deer came up to the edge of a river to get a drink. He saw himself in the water, and he was very pleased to see how large and broad his antlers were. Then he saw his legs reflected in the water, and he said to himself, "How thin and ugly my legs are!"

Suddenly a lion jumped out of the bushes and ran after the deer. The deer started to run across the open field. He was nearly out of sight of the lion when his antlers became tangled in a tree branch. The lion almost caught him. Luckily, the deer got his antlers untangled just in time.

After the deer had run a safe distance from the lion, he said to himself, "How stupid I am! I thought that my legs were thin and ugly, and yet they have saved me. I was glad that my antlers were big and broad, but because of them I almost lost my life!"

# The Sleeping Lady

## A MEXICAN FOLK TALE
### Retold by CHARNAN SIMON

Long ago, when the world was young, a princess as
beautiful as a flower lived in the valley of Mexico. She was
so lovely that princes from all over the land wanted to
marry her.

Her father, the king, was a rich and powerful man. He
had very particular ideas about whom his daughter should
wed. "It goes without saying that you must marry a prince,"
the king declared. "He must be as strong as I am strong, as
rich as I am rich, and as bold as I am bold. But most
important of all, he must be a prince from our own valley!"

The princess, who had not yet met the prince of her
dreams, just laughed. "Oh, Father," she teased, "surely no
one in our valley could be as strong and rich and bold
as you!"

Now in this valley there was a famous marketplace.
One day a young prince from across the high mountains
came visiting this market. It so happened that the princess

was also there that very same day. As she stood fingering the fine embroideries and soft woven blankets, her eyes met those of the young prince. They smiled at each other, and suddenly both felt that the sun was shining more brightly and the birds were singing more sweetly than ever before.

The prince and princess soon poured out their hearts to each other. "I will go to your father right away," declared the prince. "You must be my queen!"

But when the prince asked for the princess's hand in marriage, the king was furious. "Impossible!" he roared. "I have said it before, and I will say it again. My daughter will only marry a prince from our own valley! Now go before I have my guards throw you out!"

The princess spoke up bravely. "If he goes, then I go too, Father, for I will never part from my true love!"

This made the king even angrier. "Then go—get out of my sight! I order you to leave our valley. And I forbid any of my people to give you food or shelter. You have chosen your love—now live on it!"

24

So the prince and princess left the wide valley. As they crossed the high mountains, the prince tried to reassure his princess. "My father will take us in. You'll see. And in time your father will soften. Everything will be all right."

But when they reached his father's court, they were turned away again. "What?" cried the prince's father. "Marry a girl from another valley? What can you be thinking of? You bring shame upon our people!"

Once again the prince and princess set out on their sad wanderings. Wherever they went, through cold and wind and rain, not a soul would give them food or shelter. They grew weaker and weaker. Finally a night came when they felt they could go no farther.

"Come," said the prince. "You are cold. Lie down here and rest. I will watch over you and build a fire to keep you warm. Whatever happens, we two shall be together."

So he built a fire, and the princess stretched out beside it under the cold stars. All night long the prince sat tending the fire and watching over his princess. Finally, just before dawn, he too slept.

But when morning came, the prince and princess were no longer there. Gods from the spirit world had taken pity on their youth and their great love. Where the princess had lain, there was a mountain in the shape of a sleeping woman. It was covered with a soft blanket of snow, as if to make sure the princess would never be cold again. Where the prince had sat tending his fire, there was a taller, upright peak. Flame and smoke poured from its top.

The people in the land saw the two mountains where before there had been none. They called the one *Ixtaccihuatl,* which means "Sleeping Lady." They called the other *Popocatepetl,* which means "Smoking Mountain." The people of Mexico still see these mountains today. Ixtaccihuatl is covered with snow the whole year round. And Popocatepetl's flames still redden the Mexican night. The princess still sleeps, and her prince still watches over her tenderly.

# Unit Two
## Misunderstandings

# The Lion in His Den

AESOP

In the forest many years ago there lived an old lion. This lion was so old that he could no longer run and catch little animals for his food. He knew that the only way to get enough to eat was to make the other animals come to him.

So he crawled into his den and made believe that he was sick. He groaned and groaned. The little animals would hear the groans. They felt sorry for the old lion, and they would go into the den to see whether they could help him. Then the lion would snap them up for his food. In this way many animals lost their lives.

One day a fox was passing by the lion's den and heard the lion groan. The fox did not go into the den but stood in the entrance and said, "What's the matter, my friend?"

"Oh, I am very sick," replied the lion. "I will not live very long now. Come into my den so that I may say good-bye to you."

When the fox heard these words, she replied, "Please pardon me, friend lion, but I do not think I will come in. I see many paw prints pointing into your den, but I don't see any pointing out."

# Tricky Tracks

LYNN GIROUX BLUM

By "reading" tracks, you can discover exciting things about the animals that live near you. All it takes is practice.

### Finding Tracks

It's easy to find animal tracks, whether you live in the country or the city. Look in snow-covered fields and forests or along the muddy banks of streams and ponds. Firm, moist sand at a beach and soft earth of almost any kind also make good places to look for tracks.

Wherever you live, the best place to start tracking is in your own backyard. The footprints that you will find most often probably are those made by dogs and cats. Can you tell which are which?

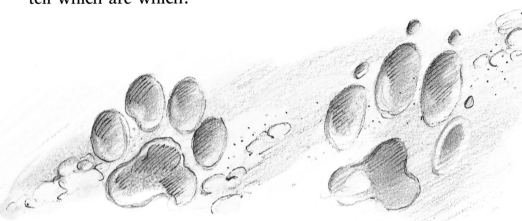

CAT                              DOG

# Identifying Animals from Tracks

Both dog and cat prints show a center pad and four toes. A dog's prints have claw marks, but a cat's claws never show in its tracks.

When a cat walks, the tracks of its hind feet fall exactly on the tracks of its front feet, so its footprints look like those of an animal with only two legs. A dog places its hind feet slightly ahead of the larger tracks made by its front feet.

The shape of a track can help you tell which animal made it. Cats and dogs walk on "tiptoes," as do bobcats, foxes, mink, and weasels. Only the center pads and toes show in their prints. Animals with hooves, such as horses, deer, moose, elk, cattle, and sheep, are also "tiptoers." A hoof is like a toenail. These animals walk on the nails of just one or two toes. A deer's hooves make tracks that look like upside-down hearts.

Some animals walk flat-footed. Bears, skunks, and porcupines place both heels and toes on the ground—just the way we do. Raccoons, beavers, and squirrels also walk on flat feet.

TOES        HOOVES        FLAT

FOX        DEER        RACCOON

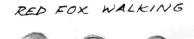

RED FOX WALKING

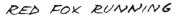

RED FOX RUNNING

## Learning from Tracks

You can learn many things from an animal's tracks even if you can't name the animal that made them. You can tell whether the animal was running, walking, hopping, looking for food, or trying to escape from another animal. You can even figure out whether the creature usually lives in trees or shrubs or on the ground.

When four-legged animals hop, their hind feet land ahead of their front feet. If the front-feet tracks are side by side, the animal that made them is one that lives in trees. Squirrels' tracks are like this.

The front-feet tracks of hopping animals that live on the ground are different. They are usually found one in front of another. Rabbits and some mice make tracks this way.

HIND

FRONT

←TAIL DRAG

DEER MOUSE
[ACTUAL SIZE]

SPARROW
[A HOPPER]

HERON
[A WALKER]

Most birds that live in trees hop along the ground. Sparrows and woodpeckers, for example, leave tracks that are side by side in pairs.

Birds that spend most of their time on the ground walk instead of hop. They leave prints that are one in front of the other. You might see the tracks of such ground birds as chickens, pheasants, quail, and herons. Robins and other thrushes both hop and walk, and their tracks often show it.

Being a wildlife detective is fun, and it's one of the best ways to learn about the habits of wild animals. With practice, you'll discover as much from an animal's tracks as you can by watching the animal itself. Happy tracking!

32

# Mandy's Grandmother

## LIESEL MOAK SKORPEN

### [ PART 1 ]

Mandy's grandmother was coming for a visit. Mandy's
mother was cleaning the house. Even the closets and
the drawers.

   "Will my grandmother peek in our drawers?"
Mandy asked.

   "Of course she won't," her mother said. "I'm just in a
mood for cleaning drawers. You wouldn't understand."

   "I don't," said Mandy.

"How will I manage?" said Mandy's mother later. "What with the baby teething and all?"

Mandy was helping her mother make the guest room bed. "That's a bad baby," she said. "All he does is cry."

"It isn't his fault," replied her mother. "You cried too when you were cutting teeth."

"I doubt it," Mandy said.

Mandy's mother smoothed the spread. She was in a hurry. She was always in a hurry now. "You'll have to help me entertain your grandmother," she said.

"I don't know how to entertain," said Mandy.

Mandy had a picture book with a grandmother in the story. That grandmother took the little girl for walks and to the zoo. She had plenty of time to hold the girl on her lap. Mandy looked at all the pictures carefully, especially the ones with the girl on the grandmother's lap. Sometimes she liked to sit on somebody's lap. Sometimes she didn't, but sometimes she really did.

On the day that her grandmother was coming, Mandy had to pick up her room, take a bath, and change her clothes. "Do I have to take down my fort?" Mandy asked.

"Oh, I suppose not," said Mandy's mother, hurrying.

Mandy put on clean jeans and her favorite sweater and her floppy old, sloppy old hat.

"Couldn't you put on a dress?" asked her mother, holding the crying baby.

"My grandmother will like my hat," said Mandy.

Mandy's grandmother came in a furry coat and a funny hat with flowers. She had two interesting boxes in her arms. Mandy's mother brought the baby down. He was crying again. "Isn't he precious?" her grandmother said. "And who is this little fellow?" she said to Mandy.

"Why, that's our Mandy," said Mandy's mother quickly.

35

"Oh, dear," said Mandy's grandmother, fumbling with her packages and trying to smile.

In the baby's box were a soft toy horse, some silly-looking suits, and a fat yellow puff that Mandy liked and wanted for herself. "I can hardly wait to see Mandy in hers," Mandy's grandmother said.

"Maybe it's cowboy clothes," Mandy thought, tearing the ribbons off her box. The dress was yellow. So was the hat. The purse had a little lace hanky inside. "Thank you," said Mandy softly but politely. She tried to smile, but it came out crooked.

The next day it rained. Mandy looked out of the kitchen window. "Yuck," she said. Mandy had the same breakfast every day: a peanut butter and banana sandwich, and tea with honey but mostly milk.

"That's not a healthy breakfast," Mandy's grandmother said. "I'll fix you some oatmeal and some eggs."

"Yuck," said Mandy. "I hate eggs."

Mandy's mother was making formula. The baby was crying in his chair. Formula stuff was spread all over the kitchen. "Do me a favor, honey," said her mother. "Go in and talk to Grandmother awhile." Mandy went in the living room.

"Show me your dolls," said Grandmother brightly. "How your mother used to love her dolls."

"I don't have dolls," said Mandy. "I don't like them. I have a frog, though," she said hopefully. "His name is

Wart." She lifted her hat, and there was Wart sleeping on her head. Mandy's grandmother screamed, her mother came running, and Mandy was sent outside.

"What I know about grandmothers," Mandy said to Wart, "is that they're very boring." Mandy was mad at everyone, even Wart. Wart hopped on the pirate ship she had built for them. "Not today, you scurvy toad," said Mandy.

Mandy's grandmother took a walk by herself down to the mailboxes and back. She walked in the wet garden, frowning at the weeds. She sat on the porch writing letters.

## PART 2

The next day Mandy's grandmother didn't come down.

"Take her up this cup of tea," Mandy's mother said.

"She doesn't like me," Mandy said.

"Of course she does," said her mother sternly. "She loves you."

Mandy knocked.

"Come in," said Mandy's grandmother softly. She was sitting by the window. Her eyes were closed.

Mandy set the tea on the table. She was thinking about the picture book, because she was feeling like sitting on somebody's lap. "I brought some tea," she said.

"Thank you, dear," Mandy's grandmother said, "but I'm not feeling very well."

Mandy saw that her grandmother had been crying. It made her stomach feel queer to think about grown-ups crying. "Tea's very good for you," she said. "It warms you up."

Mandy's grandmother closed her eyes again. She didn't take the tea.

"I think you must be very sad," said Mandy.

"I am a little sad," Mandy's grandmother said. "I was thinking about when your mother was little like you. I used to like to hold her on my lap."

"I like laps, too," said Mandy quickly. "I like laps a lot."

Mandy's grandmother held out her arms, and there was

Mandy on her lap. Mandy's arms were around her neck, and Mandy's face was pressed against her shoulder.

"Are you crying?" Mandy's grandmother asked.

"No," said Mandy, crying.

They had their breakfast together by the window. Mandy had a sandwich. Mandy's grandmother had scrambled eggs and toast. They both had tea with honey and mostly milk. After breakfast Mandy showed her grandmother the barn. She showed her the chickens and the goats and introduced her to Strawberry Pony.

"Does he bite?" her grandmother asked.

"Not if he likes you," Mandy said.

Mandy's grandmother fed him carrot sticks, and Strawberry licked her hand.

"Would you like to ride him?" Mandy asked. "Sometimes he bucks a little bit."

Mandy's grandmother thought that she wouldn't. "Hip Hip Hooray!" she shouted as Mandy and Strawberry came galloping down the lane.

Mandy showed her the pirate ship. Her grandmother took a good look at Wart, but she didn't want to hold him.

"Friends don't have to share everything," she said.

Mandy thought that over and decided she was right.

She showed her grandmother the secret blackberry bush. "Promise you'll never tell," she said. Her grandmother crossed her heart. They packed a lunch and ate it on the picnic rock halfway up the hill.

The next day was wet again. They talked a lot. Mandy's grandmother told her stories of when her mother was a little girl. About how she made cookies once with salt instead of sugar, and how she used to write poems for Grandfather's birthday, and how she fell in her uncle's pond with her Easter bonnet on.

They made popcorn by the fire. Mandy's grandmother taught her how to knit. Mandy taught her grandmother how to whistle. They had hamburgers and blackberry buckle for supper. In the evening they sat by the fire and whistled and knit.

It was time for Mandy's grandmother to go.

"Will you start casting on for me?" said Mandy. They were sitting in the airport.

"How many stitches?" her grandmother asked.

"I think about a thousand," Mandy said.

"What are we making?" her grandmother asked.

"A blanket for Strawberry," Mandy said.

Mandy's grandmother didn't laugh. She sat in her furry coat and flowered hat, waiting for the airplane to come, smiling and casting on stitches: one, two, three, four.

"I love you, Mandy," her grandmother said.

"I love you, too," said Mandy, because she did.

# The Great Minu

AN AFRICAN FOLK TALE
Retold by BETH P. WILSON

Across the ocean and far away, a poor African farmer prepared to journey to the big city of Accra in Ghana. He walked around his small farm, taking note of the yams and corn growing in the garden. Then he fed his chickens and goats, latched his thatched-roof hut, and started down the narrow, dusty road.

All morning and all afternoon the farmer trudged down the road, stopping only at midday for a bite to eat and a short rest. At last he reached the farms on the outskirts of the city. There he noticed a great herd of cows. Who could own such a great herd, he wondered. Seeing a man with them, he asked, "To whom do these cows belong?"

The man did not know the language of the farmer, who had traveled so far, so he shrugged his shoulders and said, "Minu," meaning "I do not understand."

The traveler thought Minu must be a person and exclaimed, "Mr. Minu must be very rich!"

Entering the city, the traveler saw some large new buildings in the town square. He wondered who might own these buildings. But the man he asked could not understand his question, so he also answered, "Minu."

"Good heavens!" cried the traveler. "What a rich fellow Mr. Minu must be to own all those cows and these large new buildings, too!"

Soon he came to a grand hotel surrounded by beautiful grounds and mahogany trees. A group of fashionably dressed African ladies came

down the front steps of the hotel. The traveler stepped
up to them and asked who might be the owner of
such a grand hotel. The ladies smiled and said softly,
"Minu."

"How wealthy Mr. Minu is!" exclaimed the astonished
traveler.

He wandered from one neighborhood to another and
finally came to the harbor where he saw men loading
bananas, cocoa beans, and mahogany onto a fine big ship.
With the blue sky above, the foamy green ocean below, and

the sailors rushing about on board ship, it was an impressive sight. The traveler inquired of a bystander, "To whom does this fine big ship belong?"

"Minu," replied the puzzled man who couldn't understand a word of the question.

The traveler gasped. "To the great Minu also? He is the richest man I ever heard of!"

Just as the traveler was setting out for home, he saw men carrying a coffin down the main street of Accra. A long procession of people, all dressed in black, followed the men. People on the sidelines shook their heads slowly. Sad faces looked up now and then. When the traveler asked one of the mourners the name of the dead person, he received the usual reply, "Minu."

"Mr. Minu is dead?" wailed the traveler. "Poor Mr. Minu! So he had to leave all his wealth—his great herd of cows, his large new buildings and grand hotel, and his fine, big ship—and die just like a poor person. Well, well, in the future I'll be content with my little hut, on my little farm, in my little village."

The long, dusty road back didn't seem as long as it had before. When the farmer arrived home, he unlatched the door of his hut and looked around inside. Then he climbed into his own snug bed and dreamed of the good foo-foo he would eat the next day.

# Who's In?

ELIZABETH FLEMING

"The door is shut fast
And everyone's out."
But people don't know
What they're talking about!
Says the fly on the wall,
And the flame on the coals,
And the dog on his rug,
And the mice in their holes,
And the kitten curled up,
And the spiders that spin—
"What, everyone out?
Why, everyone's in!"

47

# Sign Language

## RENA MORAN

Have you ever tried to communicate—to share thoughts, feelings, or news—without using words? If so, you may have used sign language. In sign language, gestures and hand signs are used to communicate ideas. For example, if you want to show that you like something, you may give the "thumbs up" sign. You may use the "thumbs down" sign to show that you do not like something.

Sign language is used in many sports. Baseball umpires hold both arms straight out at their sides to show that a runner is safe. A football official stands with both hands straight up in the air to show that a touchdown has been scored. In some sports, players use their hands to make a sign that looks like a capital *T*. This sign is used to ask for a time out.

48

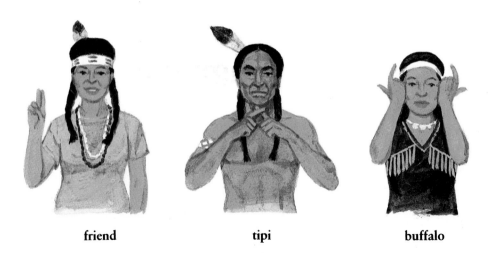

| friend | tipi | buffalo |

The Indians who lived on the Great Plains developed a sign language. It helped them communicate with other Plains Indians who did not speak the same language.

Sign language also is used by many deaf people. It allows them to communicate with other people who know sign language. In the United States many deaf people use American Sign Language, or Ameslan.

Ameslan includes about 2,000 signs. Each sign stands for one or more words. Some signs look like the thing or the action they stand for. For example, to make the sign for *ball,* you hold your hands in the shape of a ball. The sign for *drink* is made by pretending to drink from a glass or a cup.

Other signs tell something about the thing or the action they stand for. The sign for *cat* is made by stroking the thumb and index finger of each hand outward from the mouth. This is done to show the whiskers of a cat. To make the sign for *baby,* you move your arms back and forth as if you are rocking a baby.

In spoken English, people put words together to form sentences. People who use Ameslan do the same thing using signs. But the order of the signs in Ameslan may be different from the order of the words in spoken English.

Compare the following sentences. The first sentence shows the usual word order of spoken English. The second sentence shows the order in which the signs may be made in Ameslan.

I see a black cat.
Cat black see.

In the second sentence, did you notice that the word *cat* comes first? In Ameslan the first word tells what the sentence is about. Also, *black* follows *cat,* because it tells something about the cat. The words *I* and *a* are not signed at all.

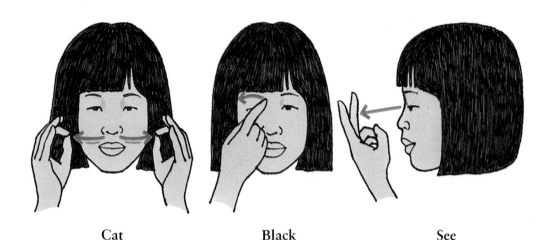

Cat        Black        See

Human beings are not the only ones who can learn to use sign language. Some chimpanzees and gorillas also have been taught Ameslan. A chimpanzee named Washoe was the first to be taught. Washoe learned the signs for more than 160 words. She used these signs to "talk" with her teachers. One of Washoe's first real sentences came about when she was playing with a toy doll. She put the doll in a cup and then signed, "Baby in my drink."

Sign language has been around as long as people have. It is one of our earliest and easiest ways of communicating. Think about that the next time you see a tiny baby learning to wave "Bye-bye"—or watch the umpire call your favorite base runner out at home plate!

# Angel Child, Dragon Child

## MICHELE MARIA SURAT

### [ PART 1 ]

My sisters skipped through the stone gate two by two. Mother was not there to skip with me. Mother was far away in Vietnam. She could not say, "Ut, my little one, be an Angel Child. Be happy in your new American school."

I hugged the wall and peeked around the corner. A boy with fire-colored hair pointed his finger. "Pajamas!" he shouted. "They wore white pajamas to school!" The American children tilted back their heads and laughed.

Somewhere, a loud bell jangled. I lost my sisters in a swirl of rushing children. "Pa-jaa-mas!" they teased.

Inside, the children did not sit together and chant as I was taught. Instead, they waved their hands and said their lessons one by one. I hid my hands, but the teacher called my name, "Nguyen Hoa."

Hoa is my true name, but I am Ut. Ut is my at-home name—a tender name for smallest daughter.

"Hoa," the teacher said slowly, "write your name, please." She pressed a chalk-piece to my hand and wrote in the air.

"I not understand," I whispered. The children twittered. The red-haired boy poked my back.

"Stand up, Pajamas!" he said.

I stood and bowed. The children screeched like bluejays.

I sat down and flipped up my desk top, hiding my angry Dragon face. Deep in my pocket, I felt Mother's gift—a small wooden matchbox with silvery edges. I took it out. When I tapped the tiny drawer, Mother's eyes peeked out at me.

In my heart, I heard the music of her voice. "Do not be angry, my smallest daughter," she said. "Be my brave little Dragon."

So all day I was brave. Finally, the bell trilled. Time for home!

As soon as he saw me, Little Quang crowed, "Ut! Ut! Ut!" I dropped my books and slung my small brother on my hip.

There he rode, tugging my hair as I sorted mint leaves and chives. Little Quang strung rice noodles from the cup hooks. Father and I laughed at this happy play.

At night, Little Quang curled tight beside me. I showed him Mother's lonely face inside the matchbox. Together we prayed, "Keep Mother safe. Send her to us soon." With Mother's picture near, we slept like Angel Children.

In this way, many days passed.

One day at school, small feathers floated past the frosty windows. "Mother," I whispered, "this is snow." My fingers danced on the desk top while I waited for the bell. When it rang, I rushed out the door.

Outside, snowflakes left wet kisses on my cheeks. "Chi Hai!" I called. "Catch some!"

"It disappears!" my sister cried.

Just as Chi Hai spoke, a snowrock stung her chin. That red-haired boy was laughing hard. Before I knew it, I was scooping up snow. I threw my snowrock and the laughing stopped.

Suddenly, the boy tackled me! We rolled in the snow, kicking and yelling, until the principal's large hand pinched my shoulder.

"Inside!" he thundered, and he marched us to our classroom.

"We can't have this fighting. You two have to help each other," ordered the principal. "Hoa, you need to speak to Raymond. Tell him about Vietnam." Raymond glared. "And you, Raymond, must learn to listen. You will write Hoa's story." Then he left the room and closed the door.

## [ PART 2 ]

"Pajamas!" Raymond hissed. He crinkled his paper and snapped his pencil in two. He hid his head in his arms.

The clock needles blurred before my eyes. No! I *would not* be an Angel Child for this cruel-hearted boy.

Then, across the room, I heard a sniffle. Raymond's shoulders jiggled like Little Quang's when he cried for Mother.

I crept over. Gently, I tugged the sad boy's sleeve.
"Raymond," I pleaded, "not cry."

Raymond's head bounced up. "Hoa!" he shouted.
"You said my name!"

"I say English," I answered proudly. "And you call me
Ut. Ut is my at-home name, from Vietnam."

"Okay, *Ut*," he mumbled, "but only if you tell me
what's in your matchbox."

"My mother," I told him.

"Why do you need your mother's picture?"
Raymond asked.

"Mother is far away," I said softly.

"She didn't come with you?"

"So many children in my family," I said. "No money for Mother to come."

"Wait," said Raymond. He grabbed a pencil and a sheet of paper. "Now tell me about Vietnam," he said.

Raymond scrawled my words in black squiggles. I crayoned pictures in the margins. When we were finished, Raymond leaned out the door. "Done!" he cried.

The principal walked up the hall. "You may go," said the big man. We dashed through the stone gate together.

The next day, the principal read our story to the whole school. "These girls sailed many oceans to be here.

They left behind their home, their friends, and most important of all, their mother. So now . . ."

"Ut's mother needs money for the long boat ride to America!" shouted a familiar voice. Raymond stood on his chair. "And we could have a fair and *earn* the money."

"A special fair! A Vietnamese fair!" my teacher exclaimed. My eyes opened wide.

"Well, what are we waiting for?" said the principal.

On the special day, I welcomed everyone to our Vietnamese fair. High above our heads, our rainbow dragon floated freely. Below, Chi Hai and her friends sold rice cakes and sesame cookies. Raymond popped balloons and won three goldfish.

By the end of the day, we had just enough money to send to Mother. "When will she come?" I wondered aloud.

Every day, we walked home wondering when Mother would come.

We slid through icy winter. We splish-splashed through spring rain. We tiptoed barefoot through the grass, still hoping she would come.

On the last day of school, Raymond and I raced home faster than all my sisters. We were the first to see Father and Little Quang at the picture window. Standing beside them was . . . Mother!

Our family was together at last.

# Love Like Salt

MARIA LEACH

One day an old king returned from a
journey and asked his three daughters whether
they were glad to see him.

"Your return is like the return of the sun,"
said the eldest.

"To see you again is like light to my eyes," said
the second.

"To have you back is as good as salt," said
the youngest.

"*What!*" said the king to his youngest daughter.
"That doesn't sound as though you love me very much."

"I love you as meat loves salt," said the little girl.

This made the king angry, and he scolded her. She was impudent, he said. But nothing could make her change her words.

So he drove her away. The king told everybody in his kingdom that he was banishing his youngest daughter because she was impudent and did not love him as much as she should.

The young princess ran out of the house into the night, but she did not know where to go. Suddenly she remembered a little house on the side of a hill where lived a kind old man who tended her father's sheep. He took her in gladly and gave her a bowl of warm milk and bread for her supper and let her lie down to sleep on a soft white sheepskin before the fire. She stayed with the old shepherd a long time after that and helped tend the sheep on the hills.

One day she heard that the king was giving a big feast at the castle. She decided that she would go there and help serve at the table. She dressed herself in the clothes of a young page and went to the kitchen.

The cook was an old friend of hers who had loved the little princess ever since she was a tiny girl.

"Don't put any salt in *anything*," the princess begged the cook. Because the cook thought the king had it coming to him, she didn't.

When the feast was served, the soup was without salt. The guests sipped it politely and said nothing, but the king was angry. He decided to speak to the cook. When the meat was served, it was tasteless. Every dish was without flavor.

So the king did send for the cook, but instead of the cook a young page came and knelt before the king. "It was my order," said the page. "I thought you did not care for salt."

"And who are you?" said the king.

"I am the child who loves the king like salt," said the girl.

With that the king gave a shout and threw his arms around her. Now he knew the value of salt, and the little princess was forgiven. The servants brought in the saltcellars; the food was salted. The feast went on, and everybody was happy.

# Nick Joins In

JOE LASKER

Nick was scared. He didn't know what to expect. Soon he would be going to school instead of having school come to him. No longer would a teacher visit his home.

Nick, who couldn't walk or run, was worried. "How will I go up and down the stairs?" he asked himself. "Will I be as smart as the other children? Will they want to play with me?"

Nick talked to his parents. "How can I go to school in my wheelchair?" he asked. "What if the kids don't like me? Will there be anyone else who can't walk?"

His mother said, "Nick, at first the other children will stare at you and ask questions. You'll all feel a little strange with each other."

"But after a while you'll get used to each other and be friends," his father said.

On and on, Nick's questions tumbled out. His parents knew this was Nick's way of getting ready for school. "We understand why you feel so worried," they said.

Nick felt a little better.

Meanwhile, the school was getting ready for Nick. Over the steps, workers built a ramp for his wheelchair. A special desk was brought into Mrs. Becker's classroom. She told her children that the desk would be used by a new boy. She told them about Nick and his wheelchair.

"Will the new boy like us?" asked Timmie.

"Will we catch what he has?" asked Nina.

"No, it's not catching," Mrs. Becker said.

On Wednesday morning a small yellow bus carried Nick to his school. A teacher's aide met the bus.

"We hope you like our school, Nick," she said. Then she pushed him up the new ramp, through big doors, and into a long hallway.

Many doors faced the hallway. If he were ever alone, Nick thought, how would he find the right door? He looked for things to help him remember where to go. The aide wheeled Nick through one door, and he knew he was in his classroom.

Everyone in the room looked at Nick. Mrs. Becker smiled at him.

"We're glad you're here," she said. Then she introduced him to the boys and girls.

Nick wondered if he'd ever remember all their names. He stared at the floor, wishing he were back home. No one spoke.

Then Mrs. Becker said, "Nick, I think the children would like to ask you some questions. Is that all right?"

Nick nodded, still looking down. Slowly his classmates gathered around.

Rachel asked the first question. "Why do you have to use a wheelchair?"

"Because I can't walk," Nick said, not looking at her.

"Why can't you walk?" asked Nina.

"Because my legs don't grow right."

"Why is that?" asked Timmie.

Nick looked at him. "I was born that way."

When Mrs. Becker thought the children had satisfied enough of their curiosity, she said, "All right, boys and girls, it's time to begin our work."

She helped Nick get settled. Then it was his turn to look around and satisfy his curiosity. Nick looked at all the children. He looked at his teacher and at the bright pictures on the walls. He looked around for a long time.

He didn't feel so scared anymore. He decided he might like school.

Days went by. Nick and the other children grew used to each other. They learned from one another.

Without being asked, people helped Nick. Nick helped people, too. Sometimes he helped the gym teacher open windows with the long window pole.

Nick loved recess. For the first time in his life he played outdoor games with children. He couldn't run, but he moved fast.

What Nick wished for most was to play ball like the others. How fast and high they jumped and darted! To Nick, that was like flying.

One afternoon there was a ball game. Higher and higher the ball went, until it landed on the roof of the gym. The ball rolled to the edge of the roof, but instead of dropping down, it stuck in the rain gutter. All the children groaned.

Timmie threw a basketball to jar the ball out of the gutter. But the ball didn't move. Nina threw a stone, but that didn't help. A teacher lifted Ben onto his shoulders, but Ben still couldn't reach high enough.

"Oh, we'll never finish our game," complained Timmie.

Nick had an idea. He wheeled away from the playground. He rode through the open gym door, past the tall gym windows, straight to the corner where the window pole was. He took the pole and wheeled back outside.

Nina saw Nick coming. "Nick to the rescue," she shouted. "In the nick of time!"

"Excuse me, please," said Nick, wheeling through the crowd. He held the slim pole tightly. No one was going to take it from him. He stopped under the gutter and looked up. He raised the pole and poked the ball loose. Down it dropped.

"Hooray for Nick!" everybody cheered.

Nick felt he was flying.

# Unit Three
## New Ways of Seeing

# A Song in a Silent World

FRANCO COUR

Wherever he went, Ludwig van Beethoven heard music. He heard music when the wind whispered through the leaves, or went *ssshh-ssshh-ssshh* across the grass, or roared from the sky to bend trees and break branches. It was as if, from the time he was born in 1770, music filled Ludwig's head and heart.

Music filled Ludwig's home too. His father sang in the royal choir of a prince in their native Germany. Many of their friends and neighbors played musical instruments, and every night they gave a concert, singing and playing music that could be heard for miles.

In fact, Ludwig's whole life was music. When he was four years old, he began taking piano lessons from his father. Soon he played the violin also. While his friends played hide-and-seek outdoors, Ludwig stayed indoors, practicing. "You must keep working," his father would say. "Someday you will be a great musician."

When he was seven, Ludwig gave his first concert, in the palace where his father sang. All the seats were filled. Ludwig looked out at the waiting faces, took a deep breath, put his strong fingers on the piano keys, and began to play.

"Bravo!" shouted the audience when he finished.

"Again! Again!" So Ludwig played again. His father was very proud.

But playing the piano and violin wasn't enough for Ludwig. There was different music inside his head. Sometimes it was so loud that it was all he could hear. He wanted to write it down so that a whole orchestra could play it. I won't just play *other* people's music, he thought. I want to write and play my *own* music. I want the whole world to be in my music.

And the whole world *was* in his music. Ludwig wrote music that was like thunderstorms and music that was like dancing. Sometimes his music sounded like armies marching to war. Sometimes it sounded like the funerals of soldiers killed fighting battles in ruined cities.

He wrote music for voices, for piano, for violin, and for whole orchestras. He wrote for every combination of instruments he could think of because he loved them all.

Soon Ludwig's music was played everywhere. He became famous and moved to Vienna, a city filled with music lovers. He was grown up by now, but in many ways he was still like a young boy. His manners were rough, his clothes often untidy or dirty. But his wonderful music made him many important friends—great noblemen and other famous musicians.

One day Ludwig heard a new sound—a strange sound. There was a buzzing in his ears. He frowned and shook his head, but the buzzing was still there. Soon it became such a roar that Ludwig was frightened. "I cannot hear my music!" he shouted. He wanted to keep playing, but all he could hear was a buzzing and a roaring in his head.

Finally he went to his doctor. The doctor looked into Ludwig's ears and held Ludwig's head and looked again into his ears. "Well?" asked Ludwig. "Can't you make that noise go away?"

Slowly, sadly, the doctor shook his head. "I'm sorry, my friend," he said. "The news is not good. The noise will

indeed go away after a while. When it does, you will hear nothing at all."

Ludwig stared at the doctor. "Nothing?" he whispered.

"You will be deaf," said the doctor gently.

"But I can't be deaf!" shouted Ludwig. "I must hear my music!" He ran from the doctor's office.

When Ludwig got home, he went to his room and slammed the door. For days no one saw him. He sat alone in his room, his head in his hands, trying to think. "My music," he said again and again. "My music!"

Then a strange thing happened. When the buzzing and roaring stopped, the music came back into Ludwig's head. The outside world was silent for him. He couldn't hear birds or the wind or the clatter of horses' hooves on the street. When people moved their lips, he couldn't hear their voices. But he could hear music inside his head.

Ludwig wrote and wrote this new music that he heard. He wrote hundreds of works for all instruments.

One day Ludwig began a new symphony. When he came to the fourth part, or *movement,* musical instruments were not enough for him. He added new "instruments"— people singing. The fourth movement of his symphony was a great song called the "Ode to Joy." It is about the joy of living in this world, despite problems like Ludwig's own deafness, or another person's blindness, or even poverty, or war.

When the new symphony was finished, word of it spread from town to town. "A great symphony!" it was called. "So beautiful!" many people said. "No symphony like it has ever been heard!"

Still, not everyone liked this new symphony because it was so huge and hard to play. Ludwig's ninth symphony was called "The Choral." Later it became known simply as "The Ninth," for it was like no other symphony in the world.

From the time he finished the ninth symphony in 1823 until the end of his life four years later, Ludwig was troubled by sickness and worry. He was completely deaf and very poor. Still, in those years he wrote some of his greatest music. He seemed to enter a new world, where no one had ever been before, and to hear music that no one else had ever imagined. Ludwig van Beethoven's music was like none ever written, and it is still beloved today, more than 150 years after his death.

# The Tiger, the Brahman, and the Jackal

## AN INDIAN FOLK TALE
### Adapted by CHARNAN SIMON

## CHARACTERS

| | |
|---|---|
| TIGER | BRAHMAN |
| CAGE (three or more actors) | BUFFALO |
| TREE | JACKAL |
| ROAD | |

SCENE: *A jungle in India.* TIGER *is in* CAGE *formed by three or more actors holding hands.* TREE *is standing to one side.* ROAD *is lying near* TREE.

TIGER: Oh, let me out of this cage! Help, someone! Anyone, help me! Let me out! (BRAHMAN *comes in.*) Oh, good, kind Brahman, please let me out of this cage!

BRAHMAN: Oh, no, friend Tiger. You would no doubt eat me if I did that.

TIGER: Not at all! I promise—I would be forever grateful to you. I would be your slave for life.

BRAHMAN: A Brahman has no need of a slave, friend.

TIGER: True, true! Of course, you are always right. Then I will go with you and do good deeds.

BRAHMAN: Once you are free, I think you will forget what you have just said.

TIGER: No, no, you are wrong. Besides, if I stay in this cage, I will die. Is that fair?

BRAHMAN: Hmm. Perhaps it isn't fair. (*Opens cage by pulling apart two of the actors' hands.*) There—you are free.

TIGER (*grabbing* BRAHMAN): Hah! Now I will eat you!

BRAHMAN: That's not fair—you promised.

TIGER: What a fool you were to believe me!

BRAHMAN: Just give me a chance, the way I gave you a chance. If I can find three things in the jungle that say you are being unfair, will you let me go?

TIGER: All right, then—ask the first three things you see, but be quick about it.

BRAHMAN (*goes to* TREE): Please, Tree, what do you think? You saw me let the tiger out of the cage. Is it fair that he should eat me?

TREE: What have you to complain about? I give shade and shelter to all who pass. And in return people tear off my branches to feed their animals. Don't whimper so!

BRAHMAN: Woe is me. *(BUFFALO comes in)* Friend Buffalo! Wait a moment, I beg you. Tell me, is this fair? Tiger was trapped, and I set him free. And now he wants to eat me. Shouldn't he be grateful instead?

BUFFALO: You are indeed a fool if you expect gratitude. Look at me! While I was young and gave milk, people treated me kindly. They fed me well. But now that I am old they put a yoke on me and give me stale food. Gratitude indeed! *(Goes out.)*

BRAHMAN: Only one more chance. Road, you are my last hope. *(ROAD sits up.)* You have seen and heard all that has happened here. What do you think? Is Tiger being unfair?

ROAD: My dear sir, how can you expect anything else? Here am I, useful to everybody, rich and poor, great and small. And what do you all do to me? Walk right over me!

All I get are the ashes from your pipes and the husks from your grain.

BRAHMAN: Alas, it appears that Tiger was right. I must prepare to be eaten. (JACKAL *comes in.*)

JACKAL: Why, what's the matter Brahman? You look as miserable as a fish out of water.

BRAHMAN: Oh, Jackal, Tiger was trapped in a cage. I let him out, and now he wants to eat me. Tree, Buffalo, and Road all say that's fair. Do you think it's fair, too?

TIGER: Wait a minute, here! You've already asked your three things. Let's get on with dinner.

JACKAL: Dinner? Whose dinner? Please, friend Tiger. I find this all so confusing. Would you mind telling me again what happened?

TIGER: Yes, I would mind! Now step aside and let me begin.

JACKAL: Oh, yes, if you would just begin again. Now let's see—Brahman was in the cage, and you came walking by.

TIGER: Pooh! What a fool you are! *I* was in the cage.

JACKAL: Oh, yes, yes, of course. I was in the cage and—no, no, that's not right. Let me see—the tiger was in the Brahman, and the cage came walking by—no, that's not it either. Well, you'd better go ahead with your dinner, for I shall never understand.

TIGER: Yes, you shall! I'll *make* you understand! Look here—I am the tiger.

JACKAL: Yes, my lord.

TIGER: And that is the Brahman.

JACKAL: Yes, my lord.

TIGER: And that is the cage.

JACKAL: Yes, my lord.

TIGER: And I was *in* the cage—do you understand?

JACKAL: Yes—no—please, my lord?

TIGER: Well, what is it now?

JACKAL: Please, my lord! *How* did you get in?

TIGER: How? Why, in the usual way, of course!

JACKAL: Oh, dear me! My head is beginning to spin again. Please don't be angry, my lord, but what is the usual way?

TIGER *(jumping into the cage)*: Like this, you foolish jackal! *Now* do you understand how it was?

JACKAL *(shutting the door by putting the actors' hands together again)*: Yes, I understand perfectly! And if you will allow me to say so, I think matters are best left as they were. Come along, Brahman. *(They go out, leaving TIGER growling in the cage.)*

# It's Showtime!

CHARNAN SIMON

The lights go down, the curtain rises, and the actors say their first lines. It's time for the play to begin! The theater is a magic place of make-believe, and you can enjoy this magic right in your own backyard or classroom.

First of all, you'll need a play to perform. You may write your own play by using a story you already know or by making up an entirely new one. If you'd rather, you may use a play that's already written, like "The Tiger, the Brahman, and the Jackal," on page 73. There are whole books in the library, full of plays you may use. When you've decided on a play, make enough copies of it for everyone who will be working in your theater. These copies of the written text are called *scripts*.

Next, you'll need a *stage,* or place to perform your play. The stage can be in a classroom, a garage, a porch—or even outdoors in the park. Just make sure you have enough space for your actors to move around. And don't forget about the people who will be watching your play! The *audience* will need room to sit, where they can see and hear everything that's going on.

*Actors* are the people who act out your play and say

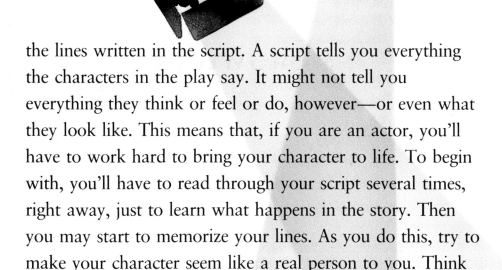

the lines written in the script. A script tells you everything the characters in the play say. It might not tell you everything they think or feel or do, however—or even what they look like. This means that, if you are an actor, you'll have to work hard to bring your character to life. To begin with, you'll have to read through your script several times, right away, just to learn what happens in the story. Then you may start to memorize your lines. As you do this, try to make your character seem like a real person to you. Think about how your character behaves in the play and how he or she would behave in real life.

Imagine you are playing the Jackal in "The Tiger, the Brahman, and the Jackal." It's hard to know how an animal would act, but you can tell from the script that the Jackal is clever and sly and quick. How would you let the audience know all this about the Jackal? How would you walk? How would you talk? What would you do while the other characters were talking? As you can see, being an actor takes a lot of energy and imagination—*and* a good, clear voice!

If you don't want to be an actor, there is still a great deal to do in your theater. For example, you could be the *director*. The director helps the actors figure out the best ways of saying their lines so that their characters will seem real. He or she tells the actors when and where to move around on the stage. The director also makes sure that the other people working on the play do their jobs right and have everything ready in time for the performance.

You could also help put together the *scenery* for your play. The scenery helps the audience know where the play takes place. For example, "The Tiger, the Brahman, and the Jackal" happens in the jungles of India. For scenery you could paint a background picture on an old sheet to hang behind your stage. Or you may be able to find some grass mats or bamboo screens to suggest an outdoor setting. The scenery can be as simple or as fancy as you like.

*Props* are things that actors use on stage to help them act out their parts. In "The Tiger, the Brahman, and the Jackal," the cage could be a prop. Right now the play calls for three or more actors to hold hands and pretend to be a cage. But you could make a cage out of a large box or use a

table or some chairs pushed together. The cage would then be a prop. If you put on a play with many props, you'll want one person to be in charge of finding the right props and taking good care of them.

If you like dressing up and are interested in clothes, you could work on the *costumes* for your play. Costumes help the audience see more clearly who the characters are. They can also help the actors feel more like their characters. Costumes can be very simple, but they should match in some way. That's so the characters will look as though they're from the same play. For example, in "The Tiger, the Brahman, and the Jackal," the actors could all wear jeans and T-shirts. The Tiger could wear a striped T-shirt, or a yellow one with black stripes sewn or pasted on. The Jackal could wear a reddish-brown T-shirt and a headband with large, pointy ears. The Brahman could dress in a long white shirt, or wear a loose cape over jeans.

Once you have decided who will act in your play and what kind of scenery, props, and costumes you want, you will need to practice putting everything together. This kind of practice is called a *rehearsal*. Rehearse your play until everyone knows exactly what to do from start to finish. That way, nobody will have to worry about where to move or what to say or which part comes next. Then you'll really be able to put yourself into your performance and enjoy yourself when showtime comes.

# Narcissa

GWENDOLYN BROOKS

Some of the girls are playing jacks.
Some are playing ball.
But small Narcissa is not playing
Anything at all.

Small Narcissa sits upon
A brick in her back yard
And looks at tiger-lilies,
And shakes her pigtails hard.

First she is an ancient queen
In pomp and purple veil.
Soon she is a singing wind.
And, next, a nightingale.

How fine to be Narcissa,
A-changing like all that!
While sitting still, as still, as still
As anyone ever sat!

# Through Grandpa's Eyes

PATRICIA MacLACHLAN

Grandpa and I walk outside, through the front yard and across the field to the river. Grandpa is blind, but he has not been blind forever. He remembers in his mind the gleam of the sun on the river, the Queen Anne's lace in the meadow, and every dahlia in his garden. He gently takes my elbow as we walk so that I can help show him the path.

"I feel a south wind," says Grandpa.

I can tell which way the wind is blowing because I see the way the tops of the trees lean. Grandpa tells by the feel of the meadow grasses and by the way his hair blows against his face.

We come to the riverbank. I see that the water is high and has cut in by the willow tree. It flows around and among the roots of the tree, making paths. I see a blackbird with a red patch on its wing, sitting on a cattail. Without thinking, I point my finger.

"What is that bird, Grandpa?" I ask excitedly.

"*Conk-a-ree*," the bird calls to us.

"A red-winged blackbird," says Grandpa promptly.

He can't see my finger pointing, but he hears the song of the bird.

"And somewhere behind the blackbird," he says, listening, "a song sparrow."

I hear a scratchy song, and I look and look until I see the earth-colored bird that Grandpa knows is here.

Nana calls from the front porch of the house.

"Nana's made hot bread for lunch," Grandpa tells me happily, "and spice tea." Spice tea is his favorite.

I close my eyes, but all I can smell is the wet earth by the river.

As we walk back to the house, Grandpa stops

suddenly. He bends his head to one side, listening. He points his finger upward.

"Honkers," he whispers.

I look up and see a flock of geese, high in the clouds, flying in a *V*.

"Canada geese," I tell him.

"Honkers," he insists. And we both laugh.

We walk up the path again and to the yard where Nana is painting the porch chairs. Grandpa smells the paint.

"What color, Nana?" he asks. "I cannot smell the color."

"Blue," I tell him, smiling. "Blue like the sky."

"Blue like the color of Grandpa's eyes," Nana says.

When he was younger, before I can remember, before he was blind, Grandpa did things the way I do. Now, when we drink tea and eat lunch on the porch, Grandpa pours his own cup of tea by putting his finger just inside the rim of the cup to tell him when it is full. He never burns his finger. Afterward, when I wash the dishes, he feels them as he dries them. He even sends some back for me to wash again.

"Next time," says Grandpa, pretending to be cross, "I wash; you dry."

In the afternoon, Grandpa, Nana, and I take our books outside to read under the apple tree. Grandpa reads his book with his fingers, feeling the raised Braille dots that tell him the words.

As he reads, Grandpa laughs out loud.

"Tell us what's funny," says Nana. "Read to us, Papa."
And he does.

Nana and I put down our books to listen. A gray
squirrel comes down the trunk of the apple tree, tail high,
and seems to listen, too. But Grandpa doesn't see him.

After supper, Grandpa turns on the television. I watch, but Grandpa listens, and the music and the words tell him when something is dangerous or funny, happy or sad.

Somehow, Grandpa knows when it is dark, and he takes me upstairs and tucks me into bed. He bends down to kiss me, his hands feeling my head.

"You need a haircut, John," he says.

Before Grandpa leaves, he pulls the light chain above my bed to turn out the light. But, by mistake, he's turned it on instead. I lie for a moment after he's gone, smiling, before I get up to turn off the light.

Then, when it is dark for me the way it is dark for Grandpa, I hear the night noises that Grandpa hears—the house creaking, the birds singing their last songs of the day, the wind rustling the tree outside my window.

Then, all of a sudden, I hear the sounds of geese overhead. They fly low over the house.

"Grandpa," I call softly, hoping he's heard them too.

"Honkers," he calls back.

"Go to sleep, John," says Nana.

Grandpa says her voice smiles to him. I test it.

"What?" I call to her.

"I said, 'Go to sleep,'" she answers.

She says it sternly. But Grandpa is right. Her voice smiles to me. I know—because I'm looking through Grandpa's eyes.

# I Asked the Little Boy Who Cannot See

ANONYMOUS

I asked the little boy who cannot see,
"And what is colour like?"
"Why, green," said he,
"Is like the rustle when the wind blows through
The forest; running water, that is blue;
And red is like a trumpet sound; and pink
Is like the smell of roses; and I think
That purple must be like a thunderstorm;
And yellow is like something soft and warm;
And white is a pleasant stillness when you lie
And dream."

# And It Is Still That Way

BYRD BAYLOR

In Arizona, Indians don't tell their stories in summer. The old people say snakes don't like to hear them. Sometimes it makes the snakes angry, and they come and bite the storyteller. So stories are saved for winter, when the snakes are sleeping.

All winter, wherever the Arizona Indians live, in some Navajo *hogan* or some Apache *wickiup,* a storyteller is speaking. On some high, rocky, Hopi *mesa* or down in the sandy Pima desert by a campfire, people sit close together listening.

Today Indian children may hear their legends while sitting in the same kind of house anybody else sits in. They

may hear them told the way anybody else hears a story told.

But the old people remember when the storyteller was so important that many other people would crowd around to listen—people of all ages. He knew the ancient songs that went with the stories, and he would move as he spoke— maybe even dance. He used chants and special voices.

And they say that firelight seemed like a part of the stories in those days. The stories were always told at night, and by the time they were ending, the fire would have burned down to embers.

Indians say no one is supposed to fall asleep while a storyteller is speaking. In the old days even the littlest children had to pay attention to every word, or the storyteller would stop. So it used to be that whenever he would pause, every person would quickly make some sign that he was listening. The Papagos always repeated the last word they had heard. The Hopis answered with a soft Hopi sound, barely louder than a breath. Each tribe had its own way of saying to the storyteller, "I am listening. Go on."

When Indian legends are told today, they never end with the feeling that they are something out of the past and finished. Instead, the storyteller will probably say, "It can happen like that now," or "We still know such things," or "And it is still that way."

So everything that went before still touches us. You can tell that in the stories told by the Arizona Indians.

# The Tricky Coyote

A PIMA INDIAN TALE
Retold by WILLIAM PENN

Coyote saw a buffalo killed. He knew it would make a fine feast for his family, so he hurried over, but a porcupine was there before him.

Coyote went up to the porcupine and said, "I saw lots of buffalo on the other side of the hill. I dragged this one over here myself, but I couldn't carry any more. You can have all you want of those others."

So the porcupine went off toward the place where Coyote pointed. As soon as he was gone, Coyote picked up the buffalo and went home.

That night the poor porcupine went to bed hungry, but Coyote's pups were having a feast.

# The Toaster

WILLIAM JAY SMITH

A silver-scaled Dragon with jaws flaming red
Sits at my elbow and toasts my bread.
I hand him fat slices, and then, one by one,
He hands them back when he sees they are done.

# Coyote and the Money Tree

A SAN CARLOS APACHE INDIAN TALE
Retold by TINA NAICHE

Coyote had some money, just a few dollars. He was walking down a road trying to figure out how to change those dollars into something more valuable.

Coming toward him were some American prospectors with their horses and mules and blankets and guns and bags of food.

Coyote had a brilliant thought. He put his money up in the branches of a tree that was growing beside the road. Then he just sat there watching the tree.

When the American prospectors rode up they asked him, "What are you doing?"

"I am watching this tree. It is very valuable," Coyote said.

"Why is it valuable? What is in that tree?" the prospectors asked.

"Money grows on that tree," Coyote said. "When I shake it, money falls out."

The prospectors laughed at him, so Coyote shook the tree a little, and one of his dollars fell out.

Now the men were very interested. "Sell us that tree," they said.

"No," Coyote said, pretending to be angry. "This is the only tree in the world that grows money."

The prospectors said, "We will give you everything we have . . . our horses and mules and everything else. We will just climb down, and you will own everything."

Coyote still pretended not to want to, and the prospectors tried to persuade him.

But after a while Coyote let them persuade him. "All right," he said. "I will sell you the tree. There is only one thing."

"Anything at all," they said.

"See those blue mountains over there? Well, you will have to wait until I get there. If you shake the tree before that, nothing will come out, and you will spoil it forever."

The prospectors agreed. So Coyote jumped on one of the horses and rode away with everything they had.

When he reached the blue mountains, the men shook the tree. Only one dollar fell out though they shook and shook and shook. That was the last dollar Coyote had put there.

Over by the blue mountains Coyote was laughing.

# The Gravestone Snake

## MARY D. BAILEY

I, Scooter Scanlon, am really good at baseball, pretty good at soccer, and can run faster than most kids. I'm horrible in art, though, so naturally I've always hated Fridays. That's the day Ms. Blinkhorn, the art teacher, takes over our fourth-grade class.

A few Fridays ago, Ms. Blinkhorn came into the room acting all excited. "Are you ready for a nice surprise, children?" she asked. Everyone but me looked happily expectant. "We're going to walk to the Old Historic Burying Ground to do some gravestone rubbing."

How low can you get? I thought. Then I remembered something that made my art-class scowl turn into a grin— the Old Burying Ground was where Gus lived! He's my garter snake—not my very own pet, but I like to watch him slither through the grass or sun himself on a big rock or just disappear under the one particular gravestone where he lives. That's when I call after him, "Aren't you glad you don't have to live in one of those glass tanks some people keep for their pet snakes?"

Yes, I was thinking, you can make today's art class very interesting, Gus. The thought cheered me up as we filed in pairs along the sidewalk. My partner this time was Carlton Stokes, the math genius, and we didn't have anything to say to each other. He was probably counting the number of steps it took to get there. Then he'd divide that number by two, take the square root, and amaze everyone with some clever answer. Carlton was good in art, too—and even in swimming. But he couldn't be perfect. Maybe he was afraid of snakes and would turn a ghastly pea green when he saw Gus.

And that Brenda Fawcett—wait until she sees Gus! She deserves a scare, after the way she made fun of my watercolor painting last week. She had no right to say my pumpkin looked as though it had been left out on a doorstep to rot.

"You can crawl over Brenda's foot for a starter, Gus," I muttered.

As we walked into the Old Burying Ground to look at the slate and fieldstone markers, I peered around eagerly. Gus wasn't anywhere in sight. I stared hard at the gravestone Gus lived under and whispered, "If you're hiding down there, please come out. Don't let me down, Gus. It's very important."

Ms. Blinkhorn didn't waste a minute getting started with the lesson. "Before I pass out the materials, children, let me tell you a little about the history of early American gravestone art," she began. "Until about 1650, only the name and the date of death were engraved. Later a skull with wings was added—and crossbones."

I started looking around, hoping to see grass moving in a wavy pattern. Hardly a blade moved. Gus wasn't there.

Ms. Blinkhorn was now up to the 1700s, talking about the face on the death's head becoming more like a cherub's.

I looked at the big, flat rock where Gus liked to sun himself. Why aren't you out in the sun today, Gus? Don't you know it might start raining tomorrow and rain for a whole week straight?

"During the 1800s," Ms. Blinkhorn went on, "the stones were much larger, with urns and willow trees replacing the skull."

I fixed my eyes on Gus's gravestone. If I could just lure him out by some strange power.

"You can always tell the age of the stone by what is engraved on it." Ms. Blinkhorn finally stopped talking.

I realized I hadn't really listened to what she'd said, so I decided I'd better watch closely while she showed how to do the rubbing. She held a piece of rice paper up against the gravestone and put little pieces of masking tape all around to hold it on. That looked easy. Then, as she rubbed the paper with a piece of black wax, a design appeared.

"Be sure to have your paper as tight as possible and rub with firm, even strokes," she said.

I took the stuff she handed to me and headed for the gravestone where Gus lived.

"You *would* take the smallest one in the whole place," Brenda sneered as she walked over to a huge stone nearby.

I gritted my teeth. What would she know about loyalty to pets? But I did wish Gus lived under a bigger gravestone.

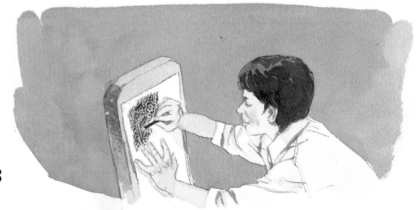

With a struggle I got the paper on and started rubbing.

Ms. Blinkhorn walked around, looking at everyone's work. "As usual, you've done an excellent job, Brenda," she commented. "That's a very clear urn and willow tree." She looked at mine. "And you've done a fine job, too, Sarah." The teachers never call me Scooter. "But I'm interested; how did you happen to select that gravestone?"

"I don't know. I guess—because—it was just here," I blurted out. I could feel my face getting hot, and my mouth felt dry the way it does when the dentist is filling a tooth. What would Ms. Blinkhorn think if she knew I had picked it because a snake lived under it, and—even worse—that I'd hoped the snake would crawl out and scare a few people? But I felt a tingly, happy feeling, too. Ms. Blinkhorn had actually said I'd done a good job on an art project. That was a first.

"Roll up your rubbings carefully, children," she said as she packed up her things. "I'm going to select the best ones for a display in the school library."

I rolled up mine as if it were made of spun gold.

The next Friday morning we went to the library during art period. I hung back, but the other kids all hurried in to see whose rubbings were on the wall. I could hear, "That's mine," "Mine's there," "Isn't Brenda's good?"

Maybe, just maybe, mine was put up, too, I thought. Ms. Blinkhorn had said it was good. I went in and held my breath as I looked at every single rubbing all the way down the wall. Not even the last one was mine.

"Look where Scooter's rubbing is!" I heard someone exclaim.

I turned around and gasped. There it was—all by itself—on the table reserved for outstanding items. Underneath was a card that read, "A rubbing of the Oldest Gravestone in the Old Historic Burying Ground, by Sarah Scanlon."

Gus hadn't let me down after all. For one glorious day I was Sarah da Vinci Picasso Scanlon.

# Unit Four
## Challenges

# Play

FRANK ASCH

Come play with me said the sun,
come play with me said the earth,
come play with me said the sky.
What shall we play said I?

Let's fly a kite said the sun,
stand on me said the earth,
I'll bring the wind said the sky,
I'll hold the string said I.

# Mary of Mile 18

## ANN BLADES

## [ PART 1 ]

It is a cold winter in northern British Columbia. At the Fehr farm snow has covered the ground since early November, and it will not melt until May.

One clear night in February the northern lights flash across the sky. Mary Fehr goes to the window to watch and listen. She hears a crackling sound and smiles. Mary likes to pretend that if she hears the music of the lights, the next day will bring something special.

The next morning Mary Fehr wakes up happy. She pulls on her boots, hat, heavy coat, and mitts, and walks to the henhouse to feed the chickens. One winter day is so much like the next. What could happen?

Mary feeds the chickens and starts back. Seeing the house reminds her of another special day, the day her father finished building it. He was so proud. When the family first moved to the farm, they lived in the shack where the grain is now kept. Before that they lived in town, but Mary does not remember so far back.

Mary's mother has told her of the comforts of town: water taps, electricity, telephones, and television. Here, water is brought into the house a pail at a time. The bathroom is an outhouse, and the bathtub is a big bucket. The family has a transistor radio to listen to, but Mrs. Fehr gets lonely sometimes.

The closest neighbors are the Bergens, and their farm is two miles away.

Mary sees her father near the barn. The caterpillar was damaged yesterday, and he is trying to fix it. Every winter day when it does not snow, Mr. Fehr likes to clear a little more land. He uses the cat to push the trees down and into piles.

When summer comes, all the family will pick roots, tearing them out of the earth with their hands so that the land can be planted.

"When we clear most of this land, the government will give us the deed to it," her father explained. "This is why we have moved north—so that we can have our own farm and live our own way."

Usually Mary likes this time just before they set out for school. Mr. Fehr has come in and is playing with little Eva. Isaac and Jake are looking at a book from the class library. This morning Sarah tries to get Mary to crayon with her, but Mary can't keep her mind on it. What could happen today?

After breakfast Mr. Fehr goes out and starts the engine of the truck. Then Mary, Sarah, Jake, and Isaac come out and crowd into the seat beside him. It is a tight squeeze, but it is also nice and warm.

Today the teacher, Mrs. Burns, has turned the oil heater on high, but the room is still so cold that the children sitting beside the windows keep their coats on and edge closer to the heater. At three o'clock Mary helps dress the smaller children. She ties their scarves over their heads and across their faces to protect them from the cold.

Mary sighs as she pulls on her own overshoes. School is over for the day, and still nothing special has happened.

In the truck on the way home, Mr. Fehr listens to the children talk about school but does not talk himself. He is watching the road carefully. Snow is drifting, and it is hard to see.

Then, just as they stop at their farm, Mary sees something in the snow and cries, "Look, a puppy." She runs to him, kneels down, and the puppy licks her mitt.

Mary carries the pup to the truck. "Please, Father, may I keep him?"

Mr. Fehr shakes his head. "You know the rules. Our animals must work for us or give us food."

Mary protests, "A dog can help . . ."

Mr. Fehr interrupts. "That isn't a regular dog. He's part wolf, and wolf pups are useless. Take him into the woods and leave him. Come on, the rest of you. Chores."

Sadly Mary goes off with the pup while the others go about their jobs. The pup snuggles in Mary's arms as she carries him into the woods. How she wishes she could keep him! "I would call you Wolf," she says.

# [ PART 2 ]

Mary decides to walk to the Bergen farm. "Perhaps Mr. Bergen will let his children keep you," she says, putting Wolf down near the Bergens' door. "Then I can see you sometimes."

That was something special, all right, Mary thinks as she walks home, but it didn't last for long. As she begins to run home in the cold night, her toes and fingertips sting, and the air burns her throat.

The family is at the supper table when she gets back. Her mother looks up and says, "We have your favorite supper tonight, Mary. Moose steak."

"I don't want to eat, Mother."

Mrs. Fehr starts to object, but Mr. Fehr stops her. "Let the girl go to bed without eating if she wants to." His voice is angry. "She should not have asked to keep the animal. She knows the rules."

Mary gets into bed and buries her head in her pillow. "Why should he be so angry?" she wonders. Then she remembers what her mother once told her. "Your father gives you everything he can. When you ask for more, it hurts him to refuse. That is why he gets angry."

Mary lies thinking about this until she falls asleep.

That night when everyone in the Fehr house is asleep, a coyote comes out of the woods. He sniffs at all the buildings and then stops at the henhouse. Silently he paws at the rope that holds the door shut, and the rope comes loose. The coyote pushes the door to enter the henhouse and get at the chickens.

Suddenly, a shrill screech goes up in the night. Everyone in the Fehr house wakes up. Mr. Fehr throws his clothes on quickly, grabs his gun, and goes out.

The rest of the family get up and crowd around the window to see what is happening. All except Mary. She hears Isaac say, "It's just a coyote," and she tries to go back to sleep so that she won't have to think about little Wolf out in the woods.

Mr. Fehr sees the coyote in the bright light from the snow. He aims his gun and fires. His shot misses, and the coyote takes off and disappears over the hill.

Mr. Fehr goes to the henhouse to make sure the chickens are all right. He is about to return to the house when he sees something at his feet.

It is the wolf pup wagging his tail.

"So it was you who warned us," Mr. Fehr says. "Tough little fellow, aren't you? Not afraid of cold or coyotes. Maybe you will earn your keep after all."

He carries the pup into the house. Mrs. Fehr has lit the oil lamp, and everyone is waiting for him, except Mary. Mr. Fehr puts his finger to his lips as a sign for them to be silent. He goes to the bedroom.

Mary looks up as her father comes into the bedroom. He puts the wolf pup down on the bed. "This little fellow would like to get warm," he says.

Mary can hardly believe she is not dreaming as she takes little Wolf in her arms. "May I keep him?" she asks.

"I suppose so," her father answers gruffly.

In the doorway of the bedroom Isaac and Jake and Sarah and Mrs. Fehr, holding Eva in her arms, are all standing watching and smiling.

# I Am the Running Girl

ARNOLD ADOFF

i am the running girl
        there are walking girls
           and jogging
    girls
        in the streets

        girls who ride their
             bikes
        and hike along brown
        country roads with
             brothers
        and their friends
        and pull wild flowers
           for their hair
        but

i am the running girl
        there in the moving day
        and i cannot stop to
             say
        hello

111

# The Boy Who Flew Too Close to the Sun

## A GREEK MYTH

Once, long ago, in the country of Greece, there lived a man called Daedalus. The name Daedalus means "cunning worker," and that is exactly what this man was. He could design and build almost anything, and his skill as an inventor was known far and wide.

Now it happened that on the nearby island of Crete there lived a wicked king named Minos. This king had in his keeping a strange monster called the Minotaur. The Minotaur was half man and half bull and was known to feed on human flesh.

Because the Minotaur was such a dreadful monster, King Minos needed a special place to keep it, a place from which it could not escape, so the king called upon Daedalus to build him a labyrinth. A labyrinth is a kind of maze, a place with many winding passageways. Once you are in it, it is almost impossible to find your way out again.

Daedalus agreed to build a labyrinth for Minos, and so he sailed across the sea from Greece to Crete with his young son, Icarus. Once in Crete, he built such a splendid labyrinth that the Minotaur could roam and roam but could never escape.

At first King Minos was pleased, and he praised Daedalus for his work. But when Daedalus wanted to leave Crete, Minos refused. He had Daedalus and Icarus shut up in a tall tower.

Daedalus and Icarus were able to get out of the tower, but there was no way to escape from the island. Daedalus knew that King Minos kept a careful watch on all the ships leaving his harbor.

Finally Daedalus had an idea. He said to Icarus, "Minos may control the land and the sea, but he does not rule the air. I will try that way."

Daedalus and Icarus began collecting feathers. When they had enough, Daedalus set to work making wings for himself and his son. He used wax and thread to fasten the feathers together until the wings looked like those of a real bird. All the while Icarus played about his father's feet, sometimes helping, and sometimes getting in the way, as young boys will.

When at last the wings were finished, Daedalus tied one pair to his son's arms and one pair to his own. Then he said, "Icarus, my son, you must listen carefully to me now.

Do not fly either too high or too low. If you go too low, you may fall into the sea and drown. If you fly too high, the sun will melt the wax that holds your wings together. Keep near me, and you will be safe."

Then they began flapping their wings. At once they rose into the air, and soon they were high above their island prison. People in the fields below watched with amazement. Surely the two must be gods to fly in such a manner!

As they flew out over the sea, Icarus forgot his father's warning. The joy of flying was so great that he could not help soaring higher and higher. Soon the heat of the sun began to melt the wax holding his wings together. Feathers began to fall off, and his wings came apart.

Down and down Icarus fell. He flapped his arms, but there were no more feathers to hold him up. Even as he cried out to his father, he fell into the sea and was swallowed up by the waves.

By the time Daedalus saw what was happening, it was too late. Only a few feathers from his son's wings floated on the water. He knew that Icarus had drowned.

Heartbroken, Daedalus flew to the nearest shore. He named this land Icaria in memory of his child. Then he flew to Sicily, where the king made him welcome.

Daedalus put away his wings and never tried to fly again. For the rest of his life he grieved over the loss of his son. How he wished that Icarus had heeded his warning!

# Boa Constrictor

SHEL SILVERSTEIN

Oh, I'm being eaten
By a boa constrictor,
A boa constrictor,
A boa constrictor,
I'm being eaten by a boa constrictor,
And I don't like it—one bit.
Well, what do you know?
It's nibblin' my toe.
Oh, gee,
It's up to my knee.
Oh my,
It's up to my thigh.
Oh, fiddle,
It's up to my middle.
Oh, heck,
It's up to my neck.
Oh, dread,
It's upmmmmmmmmmmmffffffffff. . .

# Winnie-the-Pooh

A. A. MILNE

### [ PART 1 ]

Edward Bear, known to his friends as Winnie-the-Pooh, or
Pooh for short, was walking through the forest one day,
humming proudly to himself. He had made up a little hum
that very morning, as he was doing his Stoutness Exercises
in front of the glass:

> *Tra-la-la, tra-la-la,*

as he stretched up as high as he could go, and then

> *Tra-la-la, tra-la—oh, help!—la,*

as he tried to reach his toes. After breakfast he had said it
over and over to himself until he had learned it all by heart,
and now he was humming it right through, properly.
It went like this:

> *Tra-la-la, tra-la-la,*
> *Tra-la-la, tra-la-la,*
> *Rum-tum-tiddle-um-tum.*
> *Tiddle-iddle, tiddle-iddle,*
> *Tiddle-iddle, tiddle-iddle,*
> *Rum-tum-tum-tiddle-um.*

Well, he was humming this hum to himself and walking along gaily, wondering what everybody else was doing and what it felt like being somebody else, when suddenly he came to a sandy bank, and in the bank was a large hole.

"Aha!" said Pooh. *(Rum-tum-tiddle-um-tum.)* "If I know anything about anything, that hole means Rabbit," he said, "and Rabbit means Company," he said, "and Company means Food and Listening-to-Me-Humming and such like. *Rum-tum-tum-tiddle-um.*"

So he bent down, put his head into the hole, and called out: "Is anybody at home?"

There was a sudden scuffling noise from inside the hole, and then silence.

"What I said was, 'Is anybody at home?'" called out Pooh very loudly.

"No!" said a voice; and then added, "You needn't shout so loud. I heard you quite well the first time."

"Bother!" said Pooh. "Isn't there anybody here at all?"

"Nobody."

Winnie-the-Pooh took his head out of the hole and thought for a little, and he thought to himself, "There must be somebody there, because somebody must have *said,* 'Nobody.'" So he put his head back in the hole and said: "Hallo, Rabbit, isn't that you?"

"No," said Rabbit, in a different sort of voice this time.

"But isn't that Rabbit's voice?"

"I don't *think* so," said Rabbit. "It isn't meant to be."

"Oh!" said Pooh.

He took his head out of the hole and had another

think, and then he put it back, and said: "Well, could you very kindly tell me where Rabbit is?"

"He has gone to see his friend Pooh Bear, who is a great friend of his."

"But this *is* Me!" said Bear, very much surprised.

"What sort of Me?"

"Pooh Bear."

"Are you sure?" said Rabbit, still more surprised.

"Quite, quite sure," said Pooh.

"Oh, well, then, come in."

So Pooh pushed and pushed and pushed his way through the hole, and at last he got in.

"You were quite right," said Rabbit, looking at him all over. "It *is* you. Glad to see you."

"Who did you think it was?"

"Well, I wasn't sure. You know how it is in the Forest. One can't have *anybody* coming into one's house. One has to be careful. What about a mouthful of something?"

Pooh always liked a little something at eleven o'clock in the morning, and he was very glad to see Rabbit getting out the plates and mugs; and when Rabbit said, "Honey or condensed milk with your bread?" he was so excited that he said, "Both," and then, so as not to seem greedy, he added, "But don't bother about the bread, please." And for a long time after that he said nothing . . . until at last, humming to himself in a rather sticky voice, he got up, shook Rabbit lovingly by the paw, and said that he must be going on.

"Must you?" said Rabbit politely.

"Well," said Pooh, "I could stay a little longer if it—if you—" and he tried very hard to look in the direction of the larder.

"As a matter of fact," said Rabbit, "I was going out myself directly."

"Oh, well, then, I'll be going on. Good-bye."

"Well, good-bye, if you're sure you won't have any more."

"*Is* there any more?" asked Pooh quickly.

Rabbit took the covers off the dishes and said, "No, there wasn't."

"I thought not," said Pooh, nodding to himself. "Well, good-bye. I must be going on."

So he started to climb out of the hole. He pulled with his front paws, and pushed with his back paws, and in a little while his nose was out in the open again . . . and then his ears . . . and then his front paws . . . and then his shoulders . . . and then—

"Oh, help!" said Pooh. "I'd better go back."

"Oh, bother!" said Pooh. "I shall have to go on."

"I can't do that either!" said Pooh. "Oh, help *and* bother!"

Now by this time Rabbit wanted to go for a walk too, and finding the front door full, he went out by the back door, and came round to Pooh, and looked at him.

"Hallo, are you stuck?" he asked.

"N-no," said Pooh carelessly. "Just resting and thinking and humming to myself."

"Here, give us a paw."

Pooh Bear stretched out a paw, and Rabbit pulled and pulled and pulled. . . .

"*Ow!*" cried Pooh. "You're hurting!"

"The fact is," said Rabbit, "you're stuck!"

"It all comes," said Pooh crossly, "of not having front doors big enough."

"It all comes," said Rabbit sternly, "of eating too much. I thought at the time," said Rabbit, "only I didn't like to say anything," said Rabbit, "that one of us was eating too much," said Rabbit, "and I knew it wasn't *me,*" he said. "Well, well, I shall go and fetch Christopher Robin."

## [ PART 2 ]

Christopher Robin lived at the other end of the Forest, and when he came back with Rabbit and saw the front half of Pooh, he said, "Silly old Bear," in such a loving voice that everybody felt quite hopeful again.

"I was just beginning to think," said Bear, sniffing slightly, "that Rabbit might never be able to use his front door again. And I should *hate* that," he said.

"So should I," said Rabbit.

"Use his front door again?" said Christopher Robin. "Of course he'll use his front door again."

"Good," said Rabbit.

"If we can't pull you out, Pooh, we might push you back."

Rabbit scratched his whiskers thoughtfully and pointed out that when once Pooh was pushed back, he was back, and of course nobody was more glad to see Pooh than *he* was, still there it was, some lived in trees and some lived underground, and—

"You mean I'd *never* get out?" said Pooh.

"I mean," said Rabbit, "that having got *so* far, it seems a pity to waste it."

Christopher Robin nodded.

"Then there's only one thing to be done," he said. "We shall have to wait for you to get thin again."

"How long does getting thin take?" asked Pooh anxiously.

"About a week, I should think."

"But I can't stay here for a *week*."

"You can *stay* here all right, silly old Bear. It's getting you out which is so difficult."

"We'll read to you," said Rabbit cheerfully. "And I hope it won't snow," he added. "And I say, old fellow, you're taking up a good deal of room in my house—*do* you mind if I use your back legs as a towel-horse? Because, I mean, there they are—doing nothing—and it would be very convenient just to hang the towels on them."

"A week!" said Pooh gloomily. "*What about meals?*"

"I'm afraid no meals," said Christopher Robin, "because of getting thin quicker. But we *will* read to you."

Bear began to sigh and then found he couldn't because he was so tightly stuck, and a tear rolled down his eye, as he said: "Then would you read a Sustaining Book, such as would help and comfort a Wedged Bear in Great Tightness?"

So for a week Christopher Robin read that sort of book at the north end of Pooh, and Rabbit hung his washing on the south end—and in between Bear felt himself getting slenderer and slenderer. And at the end of the week Christopher Robin said, *"Now!"*

So he took hold of Pooh's front paws, and Rabbit took hold of Christopher Robin, and all Rabbit's friends and relations took hold of Rabbit, and they all pulled together. . . .

And for a long time Pooh only said "*Ow!*" . . .

And "*Oh!*" . . .

And then, all of a sudden, he said *"Pop!"* just as if a cork were coming out of a bottle.

And Christopher Robin and Rabbit and all Rabbit's friends and relations went head-over-heels backwards . . . and on the top of them came Winnie-the-Pooh—free!

So, with a nod of thanks to his friends, he went on with his walk through the forest, humming proudly to himself. But Christopher Robin looked after him lovingly, and said to himself, "Silly old Bear!"

# The Magic Voice of Leontyne Price

SHEILAGH S. OGILVIE

Leontyne Price must have been born to make music. Her mother sang like a bird—in church, over the ironing, hanging out the clothes. When Leontyne was only three, she loved playing her toy piano. When she was five, she began taking piano lessons from Hattie McInnis, a music teacher in town. For Leontyne's sixth birthday, her parents bought a second-hand piano. Finally Leontyne had her own real piano!

Leontyne's mother had her mind made up from the start. Her children were going to amount to something! That wasn't easy for black people in Laurel, Mississippi, in the 1930s. The Prices were poor, like most of their neighbors. When there was no cash for piano lessons, Mrs. Price paid for them in washing and ironing. "I didn't know I was poor," says Leontyne. "We were rich in love and faith and respect for our fellow men."

When Leontyne was nine, her mother took her to hear Marian Anderson sing. Marian Anderson was a wonderful

singer. She was famous all over the world, and like Leontyne, she was black. Right away, Leontyne decided that she would someday be a singer like Marian Anderson.

But first she had some growing up to do. She got straight A's in all her school work. She played the piano and the organ in church. She loved to sing and to perform. She was the star of many of her school programs.

It was already plain that Leontyne was bright and talented, so her parents borrowed money to send her to college. At the age of seventeen Leontyne took the train to Wilberforce College in Ohio. It was hard to leave home, but she knew she had to go. She was going to learn to teach music.

Besides going to classes, Leontyne worked part-time at Wilberforce. Still, she always found time to sing. Her teachers kept telling her how good her voice was. At last she realized it was true.

Leontyne didn't go home to teach music after all. Instead, she won a scholarship to the Juilliard School of Music in New York City. Her parents were thrilled, but they didn't have enough money to send Leontyne to New York. It was then that the Chisholms, her neighbors in Laurel, had a chance to help. They had loved Leontyne for years, and they knew that her voice was worth training. They were happy to give her the money she needed to keep studying music.

So Leontyne was off again, this time to New York. She still had much to learn. Her teacher at Juilliard, Florence Kimball Page, helped train Leontyne's voice. She also helped Leontyne get used to her new life in the big city. Florence Page was as much a friend as a teacher.

Now Leontyne's whole life was music. She sang in class. She sang in her room. She sang at Sunday suppers. When the students put on an opera called *Falstaff*, she sang in that too. She was so good that the composer Virgil Thomson asked her to sing in an opera he had written. An opera is a play that is sung instead of spoken. Singers in an opera must be able to sing and act at the same time. Leontyne found that she was very good at opera—and that she loved singing this kind of music!

This was the real beginning of Leontyne's career. After that, she sang in one opera after another. One day she was asked to try out her voice at Carnegie Hall in New York City. Herbert von Karajan, the famous conductor, was there. He was so excited by Leontyne's singing that he hopped up onto the stage and played the piano for her himself!

In the next years Leontyne sang all over the world. Everyone who loved opera was talking about her voice. At last, in 1961, she was asked to sing at the Metropolitan Opera House in New York City. The "Met," as it is called, is one of the best-known opera houses in the world. No black person before Marian Anderson in 1955 had ever sung a major role there. It was the beginning of new times for Leontyne Price and for her people. Leontyne was an enormous success. When she finished singing that first night, people clapped for forty-two minutes without stopping!

In 1964 President Lyndon B. Johnson gave Leontyne the highest American civilian award, the Presidential Freedom Medal. Universities have given her special degrees to show how much they admire her. She has won eighteen Grammy awards for her records and three Emmy awards for television shows.

Leontyne Price was born with a beautiful voice. All her life she has worked to make it better. No one who has ever heard her sing will forget her rich and dramatic voice.

Florence Page, her teacher at Juilliard, insists that it's not just the years of lessons that have made Leontyne such a success. "It's her life—that solid, secure feeling she gained from the people who loved her and helped her." Leontyne is the first to agree. She has never forgotten how many people have helped her. She's especially proud of, and grateful to, her parents and her brother, George.

In 1985 Leontyne Price sang at the Met for the last time. Now she is teaching others to be better singers. Just as she did when she was a child in Laurel, Mississippi, Leontyne will continue making music wherever she goes.

# My Shadow

ROBERT LOUIS STEVENSON

I have a little shadow that goes in and out with me,
And what can be the use of him is more than I can see.
He is very, very like me from the heels up to the head;
And I see him jump before me, when I jump into my bed.

The funniest thing about him is the way he likes to grow—
Not at all like proper children, which is always very slow;
For he sometimes shoots up taller like an India-rubber ball,
And he sometimes gets so little that there's none of him at all.

One morning, very early, before the sun was up,
I rose and found the shining dew on every buttercup;
But my lazy little shadow, like an arrant sleepyhead,
Had stayed at home behind me and was fast asleep in bed.

# Alexander and His Horse

## A GREEK LEGEND

Long, long ago, a twelve-year-old boy stood in the dust of a small village in Macedonia. The hot sun beat down on him. He squinted his dark eyes against the glare. Alexander, son of King Philip of Macedonia, would be a king himself one day—and one of the greatest generals of all time. We call him Alexander the Great even today.

But just now Alexander was not thinking of being a king. It was the day of the yearly horse fair. His eyes were

on the whirl of dust in the horse field, where a tall, black stallion reared and squealed in fury and fear.

A trader from across the mountains had brought the horse to King Philip. The trader wanted a fortune in gold for the horse. For the past hour one horseman after another had tried to ride the wild creature. One after another had fallen from the stallion's back and rolled hastily away from the plunging hooves. Bucephalus was the name of the horse that was as stubborn as an ox but not nearly so gentle.

At last King Philip himself came forward. "We'll waste no more time on the beast! Take him away!"

At these words, Alexander's clear voice rang out. "What a pity! The best horse of all, just thrown away!"

His father turned to look at Alexander. "So you think you can do better than the best of my horsemen?"

Alexander spoke firmly. "I can ride the horse, yes."

"Very well. If you can, he's yours." King Philip paused. "And if you can't?"

"Then I'll pay for him myself."

"You will indeed!" said his father. Alexander would pay, no matter how long it might take. A king must learn to keep his word, whatever the cost.

Alexander dropped his cloak behind him. He had seen that the horse feared flapping things. He seemed to fear shadows too, even his own. Alexander moved forward quietly and took the bridle from the groom's sweating hand.

"Bucephalus," he called softly. "Bucephalus." The stallion shivered and then was still. Alexander turned so that they were both facing the sun. Their shadows were now behind them and out of sight. He walked slowly forward, and the horse stepped along beside him. After a moment, Alexander laid his hand on Bucephalus's back. The stallion flinched but did not shy away. Then Alexander leaped onto the horse's back. He leaned forward, leading him into a canter and then into a full gallop. Boy and horse raced out across the hot plain.

The crowd of men in the field stood silent. For a moment they thought the stallion was running away with Alexander. Then someone shouted, "Look!" Far down the field the horse was turning in a wide curve. They were coming back!

Alexander brought the stallion to a halt before King Philip and swung down to the ground. Philip set both hands on Alexander's shoulders. "My son," he said, "you must find a worthy kingdom for yourself. Macedonia is too small for you."

And he was right. Macedonia was too small for Alexander. In the years to come, men would follow the young king on his tall, black war horse to the far limits of the known world. Before he died Alexander had won the greatest empire in the world.

# Selina

## PURA BELPRÉ

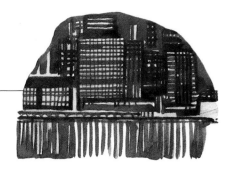

When Santiago moves with his family from Puerto Rico to New York City, he has to leave behind his beloved pet hen, Selina. Santiago likes to tell his new American friends about Selina, but his classmate Ernie doesn't believe he ever had such a hen. One day Santiago's class goes on a field trip to eat lunch by the river. On the way the group meets a man who has a beautiful white hen named Rosina. Ernie admires Rosina, and Santiago is quick to defend his own hen.

"My Selina is beautiful and smart too." said Santiago.

"Oh, you just say so," said Ernie.

"I can prove it."

"How?" Ernie wanted to know.

Santiago did not answer. Instead he turned to Ms. Taylor. "Please stop at my house for a little while. It is just down the street. I want everyone to see my Selina."

"Your Selina? I thought she was in Puerto Rico." Ms. Taylor was puzzled.

"When did she fly in from Puerto Rico?" taunted Ernie.

Santiago ignored him. "Please, Ms. Taylor," he pleaded.

"Well, it is unusual," she said. But something in Santiago's voice made her reconsider.

135

Ms. Taylor made up her mind. "All right, let us go," she said.

Santiago led the way to his house and rang the bell. His mother opened the door. She had never seen so many children at her door before. Santiago said, "This is my mother, Señora Román. My father is not here. He is working." Then he turned to his mother. "Mamá, they have come to look at Selina."

Santiago's mother was surprised, but she knew how much Selina meant to him. "Come in, come in," she said.

Everyone came in and stood waiting for a hen to appear. Santiago took the stereoscope from the table and looked through to be sure the picture was straight.

"Now you all can see my Selina. Here she is!"

"How can she be in there? What is *that?*" asked Ernie ahead of everyone. Ernie always asked things first.

"A stereoscope," answered Santiago.

"A stereo what?" asked Ernie.

"Something you use to look at pictures."

"Moving pictures?" asked the children.

"No, just pictures, like the one there now."

"Let me see! Let me see!" cried the children.

Ms. Taylor clapped her hands. "You are not at a playground. This is Santiago's home. We are his guests. Let us act accordingly."

"Oh, it's all right," said Santiago's mother.

"Only one person can look at the stereoscope at a time," said Ms. Taylor. "Make a line."

Santiago passed the stereoscope to Lucille, who was first. "I can see her from her crest to her legs. She is so colorful."

"Don't take all day. It's my turn now," said Horace. Lucille passed him the stereoscope.

"My, what a hen!" he cried. "All the colors of the rainbow."

And so the stereoscope was passed from hand to hand until it got to Ernie at the end of the line. Santiago held his breath. What would Ernie say? Ernie fixed the stereoscope to his eyes. He looked quietly for a while. He moved the

137

stereoscope ever so slowly, back and forth. "Boy, this is the queen of all queens. When you move the stereo—stereoscope slowly, the hen seems to be moving. Gee, Santiago, I wish she was really here."

"Now that *you* have passed judgment on Selina," said Ms. Taylor, "what about *me?* I would like to see her too. Goodness knows that I have listened to enough about her."

Slowly, Ernie passed her the stereoscope. She took one look. "Why, she is elegant!" she exclaimed. "You are right, Ernie; she is a queen. If I had a pet hen like this, Santiago, no one could keep me from talking about her."

Santiago beamed. Ms. Taylor put the stereoscope on the table. It was then that she noticed the large carved gourd lying next to it. "This is a work of art," she said almost to herself. But Santiago's mother heard her and joined her at the table.

"It's very old. Like the stereoscope, it has been in our family for a long time. It was carved by my grandfather, and it shows events in the history of Puerto Rico. See, here are the Indians, Columbus, Ponce de León."

The children surrounded her. "Turn it slowly and tell more about it, the way you tell me, Mamá," said Santiago. So she did, absorbed in her telling.

"It is like hearing a book read aloud," said Ms. Taylor when Señora Román had finished.

"We must go, Señora Román. This has been a day of surprises. I do want to thank you for your hospitality. It was generous of Santiago to invite us here."

"Our house is your house, but it is a fine day for eating lunch by the river. Enjoy it." Santiago's mother opened the door and the children filed out.

"*Gracias!* Thank you!" they chorused.

Once outside, they crossed the street and went skipping past the Hispanic Museum. Ahead, lunch bags swinging, feet marching to the beat of a whistling tune, went Santiago and Ernie. On down the long block they marched, on and on towards Riverside Drive and the Hudson River.

Yes, it was a very fine day indeed for eating with one's friends by the river.

# Unit Five
## Changes

# Rhyme of Rain

JOHN HOLMES

"Fifty stories more to fall,
Nothing in our way at all,"
Said a raindrop to its mate,
Falling near the Empire State.
Said the second, "Here we go!
That's Fifth Avenue below."
Said the first one, "There's a hat.
Watch me land myself on that.
Forty stories isn't far—
Thirty-seven—here we are—
Twenty, sixteen, thirteen, ten—"
"If we make this trip again,"
Said the second, "we must fall
Near a building twice as tall."
"What a time to think of that,"
Said the first, and missed the hat.

# Noah and the Ark

A STORY FROM THE BIBLE

It was a time when the world was still young, but the people in it were already wicked. They cheated and stole and lied and killed. God began to wish he'd never made them in the first place.

"I'm going to have to start all over again," he sighed. "They're not turning out the way I planned."

"Except Noah," he admitted to himself. "Noah's a good man. I'll have to give him a chance."

So God called Noah to him and said, "Noah, build yourself a boat out of gopherwood. Make it three stories high. Fill it with food. Lead in two of every kind of creature under the sun, a male and a female. Then take your wife in, and your sons, and your sons' wives."

"And Noah," he warned, "don't waste any time. It's going to rain!"

Noah figured God meant what he said, so he gathered up his three sons and they hurried and scurried about. They cut and they hammered and they polished and they painted. They built a boat as big as a hotel, with a great wide door in one side. People stood around and laughed at them, but Noah and his sons were in too much of a hurry to care.

When the ark was done, they carried food into it, box after box and bundle after bundle. Then they led in two of every kind of creature under the sun, from elephants to earthworms to creepity little ants with sour faces.

On the seventh day they climbed in themselves and waited.

Then great, black clouds flew across the sky. Lightning flared. The thunder roared and shook. In the darkness of the ark, nobody breathed or spoke. The windows of the sky opened, and rain poured down like a waterfall.

It washed over all the laughing people. It washed over the chimneys of the houses. It washed over the tips of the trees. At last it washed over the green hills and the high white mountains. Only the fish were left alive.

For forty days there was no sun. For forty nights there were no stars. For forty days and nights the rain poured down. Each time Noah looked out and about, all he could see was water. The ark rocked and tossed in the tall waves, but inside they were all snug and dry.

At last, on the fortieth day, a wind passed over the water. The rain stopped. The sun came out. The water began to drain off the earth. Just seven months from the day it all started, the ark settled high and dry on the very tip of Mount Ararat. Noah and his family came out on deck, and they all stood stretching and laughing in the sunshine.

Then Noah sent a dove out over the water. She soon flew back to the ark: she could find no dry place to land.

Seven days later he sent her out again. She flew back at
evening with an olive leaf in her beak. And when he sent her
out for a third time, she didn't come back at all. Then Noah
knew it was time to leave the ark.

Noah's sons threw open the great doors and banged the
gangplank down. Noah and his wife stepped down onto dry
land. Their sons and their sons' wives followed them. And
then the animals stepped out two by two.

As they spread out all over the empty earth, a brilliant
rainbow appeared in the sky. Then God spoke to Noah again.

"All right, Noah," he said. "You have done well. Do
you see this rainbow? It's a sign of my promise to you that
I'll never again flood the earth or make you build another
boat. Now go forth over this earth, and bring it to life again!"

And that's exactly what Noah did.

# The Dead Tree

ALVIN TRESSELT

It stood tall in the forest. For a hundred years or more, the oak tree had grown and spread its shade. Birds nested in its shelter. Squirrels made their homes in bundles of sticks and leaves held high in the branches. And in the fall they stored their winter food from acorns that fell from the tree.

Tucked under its roots, small creatures were safe from the fox and the owl. Slowly, slowly, over the years the forest soil grew deeper as the dry brown leaves, brought down by the autumn winds, decayed under the snow.

But even as the tree grew, life gnawed at its heart. Carpenter ants tunneled through the strong oak. Termites ate out hallways from top to bottom. A broken limb let a fungus enter the heartwood of the tree. A rot spread inside the healthy bark.

Year by year, the tree grew weaker as its enemies worked inside it. Each spring fewer and fewer leaves unfolded. Its great branches began to turn gray with death. Woodpeckers covered the limbs with holes, looking for the tasty grubs and beetles that had tunneled the wood. Here and there they dug bigger holes to hold their babies.

In winter storms, one by one, the great branches broke and crashed to the floor of the forest. Then there remained only the proud trunk holding its broken arms up to the sky.

Now it was the autumn weather. The days were long and lazy with yellow-gray and misty mornings, middays filled with false summer warmth, and sharp frosty nights.

Then came a day of high wind and slashing rain. As the fierce wind shrieked through the forest, the tree split off and crashed to the ground. There it lay in pieces, with only a jagged stump to mark where it had stood for so long.

The cruel days of winter followed. A family of deer mice settled into a hole that had once held a long branch. A rabbit found shelter from the cold wind in the rotted center of the trunk. The ants and termites, the sleeping grubs and fungus waited out the winter weather, under the bark and deep in the wood.

In the spring the sun warmed the forest floor. Last year's acorns sprouted to replace the fallen giant. Now

new life took over the dead tree.

Old woodpecker holes made snug homes for chipmunks. A family of raccoons lived in the hollow center of the trunk. Under the bark, the wood-eating fungus spread a ghostlike and sulphur-yellow coat. And deep inside, the carpenter ants and the termites continued their digging and eating.

On the underside, where the trunk lay half buried in the damp leaf loam, the mosses formed a soft green carpet. Fragile ferns clustered in its shadow. Mushrooms popped up out of the decaying mold. Scarlet clumps of British soldiers sprinkled the loose bark.

The years passed. The oak's hard wood grew soft. A hundred thousand grubs and beetles crawled through it. Many-legged centipedes, snails, and slugs fed on the rotting wood. And earthworms made their way through the feast.

All these creatures helped to turn the tree once more into earth.

Pale shelf fungus grew on the stump like giant clamshells, eating away and growing as the tree decayed.

A skunk came by with her babies. Sniffing at the wood, she ripped into its softness to uncover the scrambling life inside. Eagerly the skunk family feasted. Quiet forest birds scratched and picked for grubs and worms, pulling the tree apart bit by bit. The melting winter snows and soft spring rains helped to speed the rotting of the wood.

In this way, the great oak returned to the earth. There remained only a brown ghost of richer loam on the ground where the proud tree had come to rest. And new trees grew in strength from acorns that had fallen long years ago.

# A Gift for Tía Rosa

## KAREN T. TAHA

Carmela is eight years old. Her next-door neighbor, Tía Rosa,
is closer to eighty, but the two are best friends. Tía Rosa helps
Carmela with her knitting, and Carmela brings cookies to share
while they work. Now Tía Rosa is sick. It is her first day home
from the hospital, and Carmela is the first one to welcome her home.

"Carmelita, I've missed you!" said Tía Rosa. "Let's
look at what you have knitted."

Carmela handed Tía Rosa the scarf she was knitting for
her father. Tía Rosa smiled. "Your papá will be proud to
wear it," she said. "Tomorrow I'll show you how
to fringe it, and I will start on the pink baby
blanket for my granddaughter!"

Carmela laughed. "How do you
know that Pepe's wife will have a girl?"
she asked. Pepe was the oldest of Tía
Rosa's six sons.

"Because," answered Tía
Rosa with a grin, "anyone
who has six sons and no
daughters deserves a
granddaughter!"

"Now for the surprise!" Tía Rosa continued. She handed Carmela a small white box. "Go on now. See what's inside."

Carmela opened the box carefully. A snowy ball of cotton lay inside. She heard the "clish" of a chain as she lifted the surprise from under the cotton. In her hand Carmela held a tiny silver rose on a fine chain.

"Oh, Tía Rosa. It's beautiful!" exclaimed Carmela.

"The rose is so you'll remember your old Tía Rosa," she said.

"How could I forget you, Tía Rosa?" asked Carmela. "You're right here!"

Before she went home, Carmela put the rose around her neck. She promised to return the next day after school.

Carmela returned the next day, and the next, and every day for a whole week. Tía Rosa stayed in her room, and Tío Juan moved a chair by the bed for Carmela. Together the two friends worked on their surprise gifts.

"Why does Tía Rosa stay in bed all the time?" Carmela asked her father at breakfast one day.

Her father looked away for a moment. Then he took Carmela's hands in his. "Tía Rosa is very sick, Carmela. The doctors don't think she can get well," he explained.

"But Papá," said Carmela. "I have been sick lots of times. Remember when Tía Rosa stayed with me when you and Mamá had to go away?"

"Yes," answered her father. "But Tía Rosa . . ."

Carmela didn't listen. "Now I will stay with Tía Rosa until she gets well, too," she said.

Every afternoon Carmela worked on her father's scarf. With Tía Rosa's help she would have the scarf finished long before Christmas.

Tía Rosa worked on the pink baby blanket, but the needles didn't fly in her sure brown fingers the way they once did. Sometimes Tía Rosa fell asleep with her knitting still in her hands. Then Carmela would quietly put the

needles and yarn into Tía Rosa's big green knitting bag and tiptoe out of the room.

One Saturday morning when Carmela rang the doorbell, Tío Juan didn't come to the door. Carmela ran to the garage and peeked in the window. The brown station wagon was gone.

She returned home and went down the steps to the basement. Her mother was rubbing stain into the freshly sanded wood of an old desk.

"Tía Rosa isn't home," said Carmela sadly.

"I thought I heard a car in the night," said her mother. "Surely Tío Juan would have called us if . . ."

Just then the phone rang upstairs. Carmela heard footsteps creak across the floor as her father walked to answer it.

Moments later the footsteps thumped softly towards the basement door. Carmela's father came slowly down the steps. Carmela shivered when she saw his sad face. He put his arms around Carmela and her mother and hugged them close. "Tía Rosa is gone," he whispered. "She died early this morning."

"It's not true!" cried Carmela. She broke away from her mother and father and raced up the stairs. She ran out the front door and through the yard to Tía Rosa's house. She pushed the doorbell again and again. She pounded on the silent door until her fists hurt. At last she sank down on the steps.

Later her father came. With a soft hanky he brushed the tears from her cheeks. At last they walked quietly home.

The next days were long and lonely for Carmela. She didn't care that Papá's finished scarf lay hidden in her closet, bright and beautiful. She didn't want to see it. She didn't want to feel the cool, smooth knitting needles in her hands ever again.

The white house next door was busy with people coming and going. Carmela took over food her mother and father cooked, but she quickly returned home. She didn't like to see Tío Juan. Seeing Tío Juan made her miss Tía Rosa even more.

One day Carmela said to her mother, "Tía Rosa died before I could give her anything, Mamá. She taught me to knit and brought me surprises. I was going to surprise her. Now it's too late."

"Carmela, Tía Rosa didn't want her kindness returned. She wanted it passed on," said her mother. "That way a part of Tía Rosa will never die."

"But I wanted to give something to her!" shouted
Carmela. "Just to Tía Rosa. To show her that I loved her!"

"She knew that, Carmela. Every smile and hug and visit told her that you loved her," said her mother. "Now it's Tío Juan who needs our love."

"I know," answered Carmela in a soft voice, "but it's hard, Mamá. It hurts so much without Tía Rosa."

One night Carmela's mother asked Tío Juan to dinner. Carmela met him at the door. This time Carmela did not turn away when she saw his sad eyes. Instead, she hugged him tightly.

For the first time in a week, Tío Juan smiled. "Carmelita, tomorrow you must come next door. I would like you to meet my new granddaughter. Her parents have named her Rosita, little Rose, after her grandmother."

Carmela looked down at her silver rose necklace so Tío Juan would not see the tears in her eyes. Tía Rosa had known the baby would be a girl. Then Carmela remembered the unfinished blanket. "Now I know what I can give!" she said.

After dinner Tío Juan went back to the white house. A few minutes later he returned with Tía Rosa's big knitting bag. Very carefully Carmela pulled out the half-finished blanket and wound the soft pink yarn around the needle.

"Around, over, through, and pull. Around, over, through, and pull." Carmela smiled. At last she had a gift for Tía Rosa.

# When I Can Fly

MYRA COHN LIVINGSTON

When I can fly
(with my own wings)
more easily,
I will fasten them on,
open the window,
and step out into the air.
I will sail over the city
and arrive at school
on top of the roof
just when the bell rings.

The way things are now,
I put on my clothes,
run down the stairs,
open the door,
scuffle down the walk
and into the street,
counting cracks, counting blocks,
waiting for traffic lights,
passing all the stores,
and it takes so long.

When I can fly
(with my own wings),
it will be much better.

# The Magic Wings

A CHINESE FOLK TALE
Retold by DIANE WOLKSTEIN

There was once a little goose girl in China. She was a poor,
ragged thing with no mother or father. She lived with her
aunt, and every morning she led the geese out of the yard
and up into the hills. Every evening she brought them
back again.

One day in spring as she led the geese up the hill, she
saw a tiny crocus pushing its way out of the earth. The
earth was damp, for it had rained during the night. Then
from the corner of her eyes she saw another crocus, and
another. And another! She turned, and everywhere she
looked, she saw new flowers pushing their way out of
the earth.

"Hello!" they seemed to call to her. "Hello! Hello!"

The little girl started to run here and there, greeting
each new bud and flower.

"Hello!" There were lilies, irises, clover, buttercups. She
could not run fast enough to greet each of them.

Just then one of her geese flapped its wings and lifted
itself into the air. Ah, she thought, this is what I need to see
all the flowers! Wings. If I had wings, I could fly over all the
hillside and greet the spring!

Quickly she ran to a nearby brook, and cupping some

water in her hands, she wet her shoulders. Then she stood very straight in a sunny place and slowly began to flap her arms in the air.

It happened that the grocer's daughter was on her way home. When she saw the goose girl waving her arms up and down, she stopped.

"What are you doing?" she asked.

"I'm growing wings so that I can fly."

"You can't do that," the grocer's daughter said.

"Oh yes," the goose girl replied. "I've watered my shoulders, and soon my wings will sprout, and I will fly over the world to greet the spring."

"I don't believe it," the grocer's daughter said. But when she got home, she thought, If a goose girl can fly, certainly a grocer's daughter can fly.

She went into the store and poured some milk into a bucket. She went outside and wet her shoulders with the milk. Then she stood in the sun and slowly flapped her arms up and down.

A judge's daughter was about to enter the grocer's shop when she saw the grocer's daughter waving her arms up and down in the air.

"What are you doing?" she asked.

"I'm growing wings so that I can fly."

"You can't do that," said the judge's daughter.

"Oh yes. The goose girl covered her shoulders with water, but I've covered mine with milk. My wings will sprout, and I will fly over the world."

"I don't believe it," the judge's daughter said. But as she walked home, she thought, If a grocer's daughter can fly, if a goose girl can fly, certainly a judge's daughter can fly!

It was a lovely day, and the princess decided to take a stroll. When she passed the judge's daughter, standing on her terrace waving her arms in the air, she stopped.

"What are you doing?" the princess asked.

"I'm growing wings so that I can fly."

"You can't fly."

"Yes, Your Majesty. The goose girl has wet her shoulders with water. The grocer's daughter has wet her shoulders with milk. But I have wet my shoulders with wine so that my wings will sprout. Soon I shall fly over the world."

"It is not to be believed," the princess replied. But immediately she thought to herself, If a judge's daughter can fly, if a grocer's daughter can fly, if a mere goose girl can fly, then certainly a princess can fly!

The princess returned to the palace. She went into her bedroom and poured her most precious perfume onto her shoulders. Then she stood on her balcony overlooking the town and gracefully waved her arms up and down in the air. Waiting . . .

When the other girls of the town saw what the princess was doing, they stopped what they were doing and wet their shoulders. Soon all the girls were standing in sunny places, flapping their arms in the air. Waiting . . .

The Spirit in Heaven Who Grows Wings saw what was happening and decided that one girl should be allowed to fly.

The Spirit flew from one girl to another. It surveyed each girl—the goose girl, the grocer's daughter, the judge's daughter, the princess. At last, the Spirit came up behind— the little goose girl!

The goose girl felt a trembling all about her. A wind came. And suddenly she was sailing in the air, higher and higher and higher. She saw crocuses and lilies, roses and lady's-slippers, violets and daisies, star grass and buttercups.

The waiting was over. The goose girl who had wanted
to greet the spring had been chosen. All the people ran into
the meadow to watch her fly.

"It's spring!" the birds sang.

"It's spring!" the people shouted.

"Hello!" the flowers called to the goose girl.

"Hello! Hello!" she called back. "It's spring!"

# The Man in the Moon

ANONYMOUS

The Man in the Moon, as he sails the sky,
Is a very remarkable skipper.
But he made a mistake
When he tried to take
A drink of milk from the Dipper.
He dipped right into the Milky Way
And slowly and carefully filled it.
The Big Bear growled,
And the Little Bear howled,
And frightened him so, he spilled it.

# Flying

J.M. WESTRUP

I saw the moon,
One windy night,
Flying so fast—
All silvery white—
Over the sky
Like a toy balloon
Loose from its string—
A runaway moon.
The frosty stars
Went racing past,
Chasing her on
Ever so fast.
Then everyone said,
"It's the clouds that fly,
And the stars and the moon
Stand still in the sky."
But I don't mind—
I saw the moon
Sailing away
Like a toy
Balloon.

# The Planets

## SEYMOUR SIMON

The sun is an average-size star. There is nothing very special about it except that it is our star. Life on Earth depends upon the heat and light of the sun. If we were to compare the size of the sun in this photograph to that of Earth, Earth would be as big as the period that follows this sentence.

The sun is at the center of our solar system. Nine planets travel around the sun. The closest planets to the sun are Mercury, Venus, Earth, and Mars. They are sometimes called the Inner Planets. The Outer Planets are Jupiter, Saturn, Uranus, Neptune, and Pluto.

If you wanted to make a scale model of the sun and the most distant solar planet, a basketball would be the sun, and Pluto would be a grain of sand placed nearly a mile away.

Mercury is the closest planet to the sun. It is less than half the width of Earth. A long time ago Mercury had a blanket of gases around it. Mercury is so small and so hot, however, that the gases boiled away long ago. On the surface of Mercury are craters, mountains, and flat lands. The surface is much like that of our own moon.

Venus is the second planet from the sun; Earth is the third. Venus is about the same size as Earth. It comes closer to Earth than any other planet. It is covered by thick clouds of gas, which trap the heat of the sun. The trapped heat makes the surface of Venus hot enough to melt certain metals.

Venus shines very brightly. Some nights it is the first object to appear in the sky. Other nights it is the last object to disappear in the morning. Early peoples called Venus the evening star or the morning star. But Venus is not a star—it is a planet.

Mars is the fourth planet from the sun. It is a small planet, a little over half the width of Earth. Because of its reddish color in the night sky, Mars is sometimes called the Red Planet. The surface of Mars is covered with craters and mountains.

Spaceships have landed on Mars. They have found that Mars has a very thin layer of air. Some people thought that the spaceships would find life on Mars, but no traces of life have been found so far.

Mars has two moons, called Phobos and Deimos. Both of them are small lumps of rock marked with craters. Phobos travels very quickly around Mars. Someone living on Mars would see Phobos rise and set three times a day. No other moon in the solar system travels so quickly.

171

Jupiter is the fifth planet from the sun. It is the largest planet in the solar system. If Jupiter were the size of a basketball, Earth would be the size of a marble. Jupiter has at least sixteen moons—more than any other planet. It has a ring around it that is made up of large boulders and other space debris.

No one has ever seen Jupiter's surface. It is covered by clouds made of gases, hundreds of miles deep. Beneath the clouds is an enormous ocean of gases, thicker than the clouds. This ocean is thousands of miles deep. No one knows whether Jupiter has a solid core beneath that ocean of gases.

One of the strangest features of Jupiter is the Great Red Spot, which, seen through a telescope, looks like a large eye. Earth could easily fit in it. Astronomers think it is a storm of whirling gases that has lasted for hundreds of years.

Saturn is the sixth planet from the sun. It is the second largest planet. Like Jupiter, Saturn is made up mostly of gases. Saturn is large, yet it is very light.

Saturn has beautiful flat rings around its middle. The rings are made up of many, many particles of dust and ice. The particles are so close together that the rings look solid. They are so thin that they almost seem to disappear when we look at them from the edge. No one is sure why Saturn has rings. Scientists think the rings may have come from substances that were left over when Saturn was first formed.

Uranus is the seventh planet from the sun. It is much bigger than Earth, but it is so far from Earth that we can barely see it without a telescope. Uranus has five moons that we know about. None of these moons is so large as Earth's moon.

Like Jupiter and Saturn, Uranus is made up of gases. Like Saturn too, Uranus has rings around it.

Neptune, the eighth planet from the sun, is almost a twin of Uranus. It is just a bit larger than Uranus, and it is made up of the same kinds of gases. But Neptune is much farther out in space than Uranus. Neptune has two moons, as far as we know.

Most of the time Pluto is the farthest planet from the sun, but from 1979 to 1999 it will be a little closer to the sun than Neptune. Pluto is a small planet made up of rock and frozen gas. Some astronomers think that it was once a moon of Neptune. They think that the moon broke away from Neptune and began to circle the sun on its own. When that happened, Pluto became the ninth planet in the solar system.

Every day, scientists are studying our solar system. This article tells some of what they know now, but they are learning more all the time. Everything scientists learn about the other eight planets helps them better understand our own planet Earth.

# The Amazing Alphabet

SHEILAGH S. OGILVIE

A B C D E F G H I J K L M
N O P Q R S T U V W X Y Z

That's our alphabet up there. "I know that!" you say. But have you ever thought how important it is? And where it came from? And why it's just the way it is?

## The First Writing

Think of writing a message to a friend without using the alphabet. First, you could try doing it the way people did thousands of years ago, before alphabets were invented. They wrote with pictures.

The first pictures they drew were "thing pictures." The sun might look like this: ☼ . Water was often shown like this: ∿ . But that wasn't really enough. If you try it, you'll see that you can't write much of a message using only pictures of things. How would you make a thing picture for *love?* Or *wind?* Or even *in?* So people invented "idea pictures."

The first idea pictures were probably made by joining together two or more thing pictures. The thing picture for *eye* ( ) added to the thing picture for *water* ( ) made *weep* or *tear* ( ).

After a while, idea pictures could be made to mean an idea connected with a thing. An arrow ( ) could mean *enemy*. A broken arrow ( ) could mean *peace,* because you can't fight with a broken arrow.

The problem was that all of these pictures were too easy to misunderstand. One person might use certain pictures in writing a message. Another person might use different pictures to say the same thing. And the person who got the message might think it meant something it didn't. Besides, you could never tell from the pictures whether something had already happened or was going to happen.

# Ancient Writing

Something new was needed. Instead of using pictures for whole words, some people started drawing pictures that made the sound of the spoken word. That's what we do. Our alphabet is made up of "sound pictures."

It all began a long time ago with the ancient Egyptians who lived along the Nile River. They made thing pictures. Then they made idea pictures. Then they went on to sound pictures. They didn't use first one kind of picture writing and then another, however. They used them all at the same time. In the end they had about four thousand different pictures. As you can imagine, their writing was very hard to learn.

But the Phoenicians changed all that. They were great traders. Their ships carried cargoes to all the ports on the Mediterranean Sea and often even farther. They needed a good way to keep track of the things they bought and sold. Egyptian writing was far too much trouble for these busy merchants. They stripped it down until there were only sound pictures left. Then they changed those to fit the sounds of their own language. They made the pictures much simpler too. For example, the Egyptian thing picture for *ox* was . In the Phoenician language, *ox* was *aleph*. The Phoenicians drew the sound picture for *aleph* with simple lines, like this: . At some time or other, this was tipped over to make our *A*.

When the Phoenicians carried goods to other countries, they took along their alphabet too. It had only twenty-two letters. It was easy to write and easy to read. The Greeks liked the idea and decided to use it themselves. They added letters to the Phoenician alphabet and changed some of those that were already there.

The Romans admired all things Greek. They took the Greek alphabet and made their own changes. This alphabet is the one we use now.

## Modern Alphabets

Today there are about fifty different alphabets in the world. Some of them are partly like ours. The Russian alphabet came from Greece too, but it didn't pass through Rome. It has thirty-three letters in it, and some of them, like *O* and *A*, are just like ours. But they print *L* like this— ⅃ —and *D* like this— ᴫ . They have letters that look like this— Ж —and this— Щ —too.

Other alphabets aren't like ours in any way. The Chinese have just invented an alphabet, but for thousands of years they had been using pictures. Every time they needed to, they added a new picture. Sometimes it was for a thing; sometimes it was for an idea we would explain in several words. *Tree* looks like this— 木 —and 如 means *as good as.* Chinese writing is beautiful to look at but very, very hard to learn.

Our Roman alphabet is used in many languages— German, Spanish, Italian, French, and Polish, among others. The words we use aren't the same, but we all use the same letters. *Tree* in German is written *Baum,* in French it's written *arbre,* and in Spanish it's *arbol.*

Ours is an efficient alphabet. You can write anything you want just by putting twenty-six letters together in different ways.

So next time you're leaving that message for a friend, remember to be thankful for our amazing alphabet!

# A Word Is Dead

## EMILY DICKINSON

A word is dead
When it is said,
Some say.
I say it just
Begins to live
That day.

# Father Hidalgo

## HELEN WEBBER

It is 16 September—Independence Day in Mexico. Crowds have gathered in front of the president's palace in Mexico City. When the president rings the great liberty bell, an answering shout rings out from the people gathered below.

"*Viva Mexico!* Long live Mexico! Long live independence!"

As the liberty bell sings out, people hearing it remember the man who first rang it to start Mexico's fight for freedom. His full name was Father Miguel Hidalgo y Castilla, but Mexicans today know him simply as Father Hidalgo. This is the story of how he became the father of his country.

Father Hidalgo was born in Mexico in 1753. At that time Mexico had been ruled by Spain for more than two hundred years. This meant that only people who were born in Spain could make laws or decide how Mexico should be governed. Though Father Hidalgo's family had come from Spain, his heart was with the Mexican people. He did not like the way the Spanish people treated the Mexicans.

Father Hidalgo had a good job as the head of an important university. He saw, however, that the native Mexicans were suffering under Spanish rule, and he wanted to help.

So Father Hidalgo went as a priest to the little village of Dolores. He had many good ideas for helping the poor people there. He taught them how to grow grapes for making wine. He got some mulberry trees and stocked them with silkworms. Then he taught the villagers how to make silk. He thought the villagers could sell the wine and the silk. Then they would have enough money for food and clothes and education for their children.

When the Spanish rulers heard of Father Hidalgo's work, they were angry. They sent men to destroy the grapevines and mulberry trees in Dolores. Mexicans were not allowed to make wine and silk. Instead, they had to buy these things from Spain. The prices were so high, however, that only rich people could afford them.

Father Hidalgo was discouraged, but he did not give up. He thought of some new ways to help the people in his village. He started a blacksmith shop, and he gave lessons in making bricks and pottery out of clay. It took a long time, though, for the people to learn these skills. In the meantime, they were still hungry and still poor.

Now Father Hidalgo was getting angry. He began to believe that if the Mexican people were ever to be happy, they must free themselves from Spain. He began to talk to other Mexicans about his idea. He learned that many of them wanted to be free too. Together they began making plans to rise up against Spain.

Then, in September of 1810, the Spanish government found out about the Mexicans' plans to fight Spain. They were going to send soldiers to arrest Father Hidalgo!

Father Hidalgo wasn't ready to fight Spain yet, but it was too dangerous to wait any longer. At daybreak on 16 September 1810 he rang the great church bell in Dolores.

When the people gathered outside the church, Father Hidalgo spoke to them. He ended his speech with the call for independence that would be shouted throughout Mexico every September for years to come. "*Viva Mexico!* Long live Mexico! Long live independence!"

Then Father Hidalgo, followed by a dozen men of Dolores, set out to raise an army. They walked from town to town, and eventually the ragged band numbered eighty thousand men. Armed mostly with sticks, stones, knives, and axes, they set out to fight the Spanish soldiers.

At first the Mexicans won battle after battle. All over Mexico, people began to have hope that soon their country would be free from Spain. Then, just outside Mexico City, the Mexican freedom fighters were defeated by the well-trained and well-armed Spanish soldiers. Father Hidalgo himself was captured and put to death on 30 July 1811.

But the struggle for freedom did not die with Father Hidalgo. After ten more years of fighting, the Mexicans finally won their independence. In 1821 Father Hidalgo's dream for a free Mexico came true.

Today the Mexican people remember Father Hidalgo as the father of their country. To honor him they have brought the bell from the little church in Dolores to their capital, Mexico City. There, every year on 16 September, they celebrate their independence by ringing the bell and shouting what Father Hidalgo shouted so many years ago: "*Viva Mexico!*"

# A Visit from St. Nicholas

CLEMENT C. MOORE

'Twas the night before Christmas, when all through
    the house
Not a creature was stirring, not even a mouse;
The stockings were hung by the chimney with care,
In hopes that St. Nicholas soon would be there.
The children were nestled all snug in their beds,
While visions of sugar-plums danced in their heads;
And Mamma in her 'kerchief, and I in my cap,
Had just settled our brains for a long winter's nap,
When out on the lawn there arose such a clatter,
I sprang from my bed to see what was the matter.
Away to the window I flew like a flash,
Tore open the shutters and threw up the sash.
The moon on the breast of the new-fallen snow
Gave the luster of midday to objects below,
When, what to my wondering eyes should appear,
But a miniature sleigh, and eight tiny reindeer,
With a little old driver, so lively and quick,
I knew in a moment it must be St. Nick.
More rapid than eagles his coursers they came,
And he whistled, and shouted, and called them by name,

"Now, Dasher! Now, Dancer! Now, Prancer and Vixen!
On, Comet! On, Cupid! On, Donder and Blitzen!
To the top of the porch! To the top of the wall!
Now dash away! Dash away! Dash away all!"
As dry leaves that before the wild hurricane fly,
When they meet with an obstacle, mount to the sky,
So up to the housetop the coursers they flew
With the sleigh full of toys, and St. Nicholas, too.
And then, in a twinkling, I heard on the roof
The prancing and pawing of each little hoof.
As I drew in my head, and was turning around,
Down the chimney St. Nicholas came with a bound.
He was dressed all in fur, from his head to his foot,
And his clothes were all covered with ashes and soot;
A bundle of toys he had flung on his back,
And he looked like a peddler just opening his pack.
His eyes—how they twinkled! His dimples how merry!
His cheeks were like roses, his nose like a cherry!
His droll little mouth was drawn up like a bow,
And the beard on his chin was as white as the snow;
The stump of a pipe he held tight in his teeth,
And the smoke it encircled his head like a wreath;
He had a broad face and a little round belly
That shook, when he laughed, like a bowlful of jelly.
He was chubby and plump, a right jolly old elf,
And I laughed when I saw him, in spite of myself;

A wink of his eye and a twist of his head
Soon gave me to know I had nothing to dread;
He spoke not a word, but went straight to his work,
And filled all the stockings; then turned with a jerk,
And laying his finger aside of his nose
And giving a nod, up the chimney he rose;
He sprang to his sleigh, to his team gave a whistle
And away they all flew like the down of a thistle.
But I heard him exclaim, ere he drove out of sight,
"Happy Christmas to all, and to all a good night."

# Glossary

# Pronunciation Key

| | | | |
|---|---|---|---|
| a_, ă_ | apple, tan | g | gas, wiggle, sag |
| ā | acorn, table | ġ | gem, giant, gym |
| à | alone, Donna | gh_ | ghost |
| â | air, care | _gh | though, thought (silent) |
| ä | father, wand | h_ | hat |
| a̧ | all, ball | i_, ĭ_ | it, sit |
| a_e | ape, bake | ī | pilot, pie |
| ai_ | aim, sail | _ï_ | babies, machine, *also* |
| àr | calendar | | onion, savior, familiar |
| är | art, park, car | i_e | ice, bite |
| au_ | author, Paul | _igh | high, bright |
| aw | awful, lawn, saw | ir | irk, bird, fir |
| _ay | say, day | j_ | jam |
| b | bat, able, tub | k | kite, ankle, ink |
| c | cat, cot, cut | kn_ | knife |
| ce | cent, ace | l | lamp, wallet, tail |
| ch | chest, church | _le | table, ample |
| c̄h | chorus, ache | m | man, bump, ham |
| ch̆ | chute | _mb | lamb, comb |
| ci̧ | cider, decide | n | no, tent, sun |
| _ci_ | special | _n̄_ | uncle, anger |
| _ck | tack, sick | _ng | sing, ring |
| cy | bicycle | o_, ŏ_ | odd, pot |
| d | dad | ō | go, no, toe |
| _dge | edge, judge | ȯ | come, wagon |
| e_, ĕ_ | elf, hen | ô | off, song |
| ē | equal, me | oa_ | oat, soap |
| ė | moment, loaded | o_e | ode, bone |
| ea | eat, leap, tea | oi_ | oil, boil |
| _ĕa_ | head, bread | ŏo | book, nook |
| ee | eel, feet, see | o̅o̅ | boot, zoo |
| er | herd, her | or | order, normal |
| _ew | few, blew | ȯr | motor, doctor |
| f | far, taffy, off | ou_ | out, hound |

| | | | |
|---|---|---|---|
| ow | owl, town, cow | ū̱ | truth, true |
| _ōw | low, throw | u̇ | nature |
| _oy | boy, toy | u̱ | pull, full |
| p | paper, tap | ur | urge, turn, fur |
| ph | phone, elephant, graph | ūr | cure, pure |
| qu_ | quick, queen | v | voice, save |
| r | ram, born, ear | w_ | will, wash |
| s | sun, ask, yes | wh_ | white, what |
| _s̱ | toes, hose | wr_ | write |
| _s̱_ | vision, confusion | _x | extra, ax |
| ss̱ | fission | _x̱_ | exist, example |
| sh | show, bishop, fish | y_ | yes, yet |
| t | tall, sets, bit | _y | baby, happy (when |
| th | thick, three | | it is the only |
| tẖ | this, feather, bathe | | vowel in a final |
| _tch | itch, patch | | unstressed |
| _ti̱_ | nation, station, | | syllable) |
| | also question | _y̆_ | cymbal |
| ṯu | congratulate | _ȳ | cry, sky |
| u_, ŭ_ | up, bus | ẏ | zephyr, martyr |
| ū | use, cute, also granulate | z | zoo, nozzle, buzz |

1. If a word ends in a silent *e*, as in **face**, the silent *e* is not marked. If a word ends in -*ed* pronounced **t**, as in **baked**, or **d**, as in **stayed**, no mark is needed. If the ending -*ed* forms a separate syllable pronounced **ėd**, as in **load′ėd**, the *e* has a dot.

2. If there are two or three vowels in the same syllable and only one is marked, as in **beaū′ty, friĕnd, rōgue,** or **breāk,** all the other vowels in the syllable are silent.

3. The Open Court diacritical marks in the Pronunciation Key make it possible to indicate the pronunciation of most unfamiliar words without respelling.

**a·ban′don** *v.* to leave behind

**ab·sorbed′** *adj.* held in attention

**ac·cord′ing·ly** *adv.* in the way expected

**a·las′** *interj.* an old-fashioned way of saying "Oh, no!"

**Am′es·lan′** *n.* American Sign Language

**ant′lers** *n. pl.* a pair of bony, branching horns on the head of an animal

**anx·ious·ly** (**ank′shus·ly**) *adv.* with excitement (special meaning in this story)

**A·pach′ē** *n.* an American Indian tribe of the southwestern United States

**ärk** *n.* the large, roomy boat built by Noah for safety

**âr′rant** *adj.* complete; downright

**as·ton′ished** *adj.* greatly surprised

**as·tron′·o·mer** *n.* a scientist who studies the stars, planets, and outer space

**av′er·age** *adj.* not large and not small; between large and small

**band** *n.* a group of people gathered for some purpose

**ban′ish** *v.* to force to leave a place

**be·wâre** *v.* to watch out for someone or something who might cause harm

**Big Beâr** *n.* a group of stars that forms the shape of a huge animal (The Big Bear includes the group of stars called the Big Dipper.)

**black′smith** *n.* a person who makes horseshoes

**blurt** *v.* to say in a hurry without thinking

**bob′white′** *n.* a plump, brown-and-white bird; a quail

**bold** *adj.* daring or brave

**both′er** *interj.* a word that shows mild anger

**Bräh′man** *n.* a priest or other person of the highest class in India

**Braille** *n.* a kind of printing with raised dots that blind people can read by feeling with their fingers

**brä′vō** (*or* **brä·vō′**) *interj.* a shout of praise after a performance

**brī′dle** *n.* a metal and leather object that fits over a horse's nose and has straps to control the animal

**bril′liant** *adj.* very bright

**Brit′ish Cō·lum′bi·a** *n.* the most western area of Canada

**Brit′ish sol·diers** (**sōl′jers**) *n. pl.* tiny plants with green stems and red tips

**Bū·ceph′a·lus** *n.* the name of the horse of Alexander the Great

**buck** *v.* to leap upward and forward suddenly

**buck′le** *n.* a fruit dessert

**bȳ′stand·er** *n.* a person who watches nearby activity without taking part

**can′ter** *n.* the easy, running steps of a horse

**cà·reer′** *n.* a person's lifetime work

**cär′gō** *n.* goods carried from place to place

**Cär·me′lä**

**Cär·me·lï′tä** *n.* a Spanish nickname that means "little Carmela"

**Cär′ne·ġie Hạll** *n.* a building in New York City in which important concerts are given

**cast** *v.* to make [something] to fall in a certain direction

**cast on** *v.* to place the first row of stitches on a knitting needle

**cat** *n.* a short name for caterpillar (special meaning in this story— *See also* **caterpillar.**)

**cat′er·pil′làr** *n.* a kind of tractor (*See also* **cat.**)

**cat′tail** *n.* a tall, fuzzy-tipped plant that grows in wet areas

**cen′ti·pēde** *n.* a small animal that has many pairs of legs

**chant** *v.* to speak together in a singsong way

Pronunciation Key

VOWELS: sat, hăve, āble, fäther, ạll, câre, álone; yet, brĕad, mē, loadèd; it, practĭce, pīlot, machïne; hot, nō, ôff, wagòn; fŏŏt, fōōd; oil, toy; count, town; up, ūse, trụth, pụll; mȳth, baby, crȳ, zephỳr.

CONSONANTS: cent, cider, cycle; c̄horus, c̣hute; ġem; light and though (silent), ghost; iñk; elephant; toes̨; t̲hem; special, meaṣure, natịon, natụre.

**c̄har′ȧc·ter** *n.* a person in a play or story

**cher′ub** *n.* a chubby, sweet-faced angel

**Chĭ Haī**

**c̄ho′ràl** *adj.* having to do with music by a group of singers

**ci·vil′ïàn** *adj.* belonging to someone who is not a member of the armed forces

**clay** *n.* a sticky dirt that dries hard and firm

**cloak** *n.* a loose kind of outer clothing

**clus′ter** *v.* to gather together

**cȯl′ȯur** *n.* the British spelling of *color*

**com′bi·nā′tion** *n.* a group; a way of putting together

**cȯme ȯf** *v.* to result from

**cȯm′fȯrt** *n.* a thing that makes life more easy or more pleasant

**com′ment** *v.* to say what one thinks about something

**cȯm·mū′ni·cate** *v.* to exchange or pass along information or ideas

195

com·pō'ser *n.* a person who writes music

con'cert *n.* a musical performance

con·dĕnsed' *adj.* thickened; having some of the water removed

con·duc'tor *n.* a person who leads musicians

con·fūs'ing *adj.* difficult to understand

con·vēn'iĕnt *adj.* useful or handy

core *n.* the center part; the part deepest inside

cōur'ser *n.* a swift horse or other animal

crea'tùre *n.* an animal or a person

crest *n.* the feathers that stick up from the head of a bird

crim'son *adj.* deep purple-red in color

cun'ning *adj.* clever or tricky

cū'ri·os'i·ty *n.* lively interest or wondering

Daĕd'a·lus *n.* an inventor in ancient Greek stories

dah·lia (dal'ya *or* däl'ya) *n.* a kind of flower

da Vin·ci (da vin'chï) *n.* Leonardo da Vinci, a famous painter

de·bris (de·brï') *n.* rubbish

de·cay'ing *adj.* rotting

deed *n.* 1. an action 2. a legal paper saying that a person owns a certain thing

de·feat' *v.* to beat in battle

de·fend' *v.* to argue that something or someone is good

de·gree' *n.* a special title, such as Doctor, earned by completing certain studies

den *n.* a place where a wild animal lives

de·sign (de·sïn') *v.* to draw or write a plan

de·stroy' *v.* to ruin completely or to wreck

de·vel'op *v.* to bring into being

Dip'per *n.* a group of stars that form the shape of a cup with a long handle

dis·play' *n.* an exhibit of items, such as would be found in a museum

dra·mat'ic *adj.* thrilling or exciting

drift *v.* to be blowing and piling up

drōll *adj.* funny

Earth *n.* the planet that we live on

eb'on·y *n.* a hard, black wood

ef·fi'cient *adj.* able to get good results without wasting time

el'e·gant *adj.* graceful in looks; of high quality

em'ber *n.* a small piece of glowing wood or coal

em·broi'der·y *n.* a cloth that has designs sewn on it

**Em′my a·ward′** *n.* an important prize for excellence in television

**Em′pire State** *n.* a short name for the Empire State Building, a skyscraper in New York City

**en·grāve** *v.* to mark by digging out letters and figures

**en′vy** *n.* a strong feeling of wanting what another person has; the wish to take away what another person has

**ere** (âr) *prep.* a word sometimes used in poems to mean "before"

**e·ven′tū·al·ly** *adv.* after some length of time

**ex·pect′ant** *adj.* waiting for something to happen

**faith** *n.* a belief in something or someone, as in God; trust

**fash′ion·a·bly** *adv.* in the latest style

**fea′ture** *n.* an outstanding part

**field′stone′** *n.* a stone in its natural form

**Fifth Av′e·nue′** *n.* an important street in New York City

**fix** *v.* to prepare

**flâre** *v.* to burst out with a sudden, bright light

**flesh** *n.* the soft outer part of the body; meat

**foo foo** *n.* an African food

**form** *v.* to make, shape, or build

**for′mū·la** *n.* a special milk mixture for babies

**frag′ĭle** *adj.* easily damaged or hurt

**fringe** *v.* to make a row of hanging threads on the edge of cloth

**fum′ble** *v.* to handle awkwardly

**fuñ′gus** *n.* a plant that gets its food by living on other plants (A mushroom is one kind of fungus.)

**gang′plañk** *n.* a movable board used for walking onto and off a ship

**gas** *n.* a form of matter like air that is not a solid or a liquid

**ġēn′ĭus** *n.* a person who is very smart

**ġes·ture** *n.* a movement of the fingers, hands, or arms that has meaning

**Gha·na** (gä′nȧ) *n.* a country in western Africa

**ghast′ly** *adj.* horrible or pale

**glass** *n.* a mirror

**gnaw** (naw) *v.* to eat away little by little

**gō′pher·wŏŏd** *n.* a kind of wood, probably like cypress, mentioned in the Bible

**gourd** *n.* a fruit, similar to squash, that dries hard

**grä·cï·äs** *v.* the Spanish word for "thank you"

**Gram′my à·ward′** *n.* an important prize for excellence in recording

**grān′à·ry** (*or* **gran′à·ry**) *n.* a building in which grain is stored

**grat′i·tude** *n.* a feeling of thankfulness

**Greāt Plains** *n.* a large, flat area in the middle of the United States

**greed′y** *adj.* wanting more than one's fair share

**grïeve** *v.* to feel great sorrow because of a loss

**grit** *v.* to grind together

**grŏŏm** *n.* a person who takes care of horses

**grub** *n.* an insect not fully grown (A grub looks like a small, thick worm.)

**gut′ter** *n.* the curved pathway along the edge of a roof in which rainwater collects

**hā′tred** *n.* a strong feeling of dislike

**heärt′wŏŏd** *n.* the center part of a tree

**heed** *n.* to pay attention to

**His·pan′ic** *adj.* having to do with countries in which Spanish is spoken

**hoe** *n.* a garden tool for chopping up the ground

**hō′gàn** *n.* an American Indian house of branches and mud

**Hō′pï** *n.* an American Indian tribe of the southwestern United States

**hunt′er** *n.* a person who kills wild animals for food

**Ic′àr·ùs** *n.* in ancient Greek stories the boy who flew too close to the sun

**im·aġ′i·nā′tiòn** *n.* the ability to make pictures in the mind

**im·pres′sïve** *adj.* memorable

**im′pū·dènt** *adj.* rude

**in·deed′** *interj.* actually; really; in truth; in fact

**in′dex fiñ′ger** *n.* the finger next to the thumb

**in′ter·rupt′** *v.* to break in while another person is doing something

**in·ven′tòr** *n.* a person who makes something for the first time ever

**Ix·tac·ci·huatl** (ïs′täk·sï·wät′èl) *n.* a mountain in Mexico

**jack′ăl** *n.* a wild animal of Asia and Africa (A jackal looks much like a dog.)

**jag′ġėd** *adj.* having sharp points sticking out

**jañ′gle** *v.* to make an unpleasant ringing sound like that of metal

**Jūil′li·ärd′** *n.* The Juilliard School, a famous music school

**Jū′pi·ter** *n.* the largest known planet and the fifth from the sun

**ker′chĭef** *n.* a square scarf worn on the head or neck

**lab′ў·rinth** *n.* a group of paths arranged so that finding the way out is difficult

**lär′der** *n.* a place where food is stored

**latch** *v.* to fasten a door closed

**leġ′ėnd** *n.* a story handed down from times long ago

**Lit′tle Beâr** *n.* the name of a group of stars that forms the shape of a wild animal (The Little Bear includes the group of stars that form the Little Dipper.)

**loam** *n.* a soil made up of leaves and other plant parts

**lord** *n.* an honored person

**Lud·wig van Bee·tho·ven** (lōod′vig vän bā′tō·ven) *n.* a famous German writer of music

**Pronunciation Key**

VOWELS: sat, hăve, āble, fäther, a̱ll, câre, ȧlone; yet, brĕad, mē, loadėd; it, practĭce, pīlot, machïne; hot, nō, ôff, wagȯn; fo̅o̅t, fo̅o̅d; oil, toy; count, town; up, ūse, tru̱th, pṵll; mȳth, baby, crȳ, zephȳr.

CONSONANTS: cent, cider, cycle; c̄horus, c̱hute; ġem; light and though (silent), ghost; iñk; elephant; toe̱s; ṯhem; special, mea̱s̱ure, nati̱on, natu̱re.

**lūre** *v.* to convince a person to act

**lus′ter** *n.* a brightness or a soft shine

**Mă′cė·dō′nï·ȧ** *n.* an ancient country to the north of Greece

**mȧ·hog′ȧ·ny** *n.* a very hard, reddish African wood

**mā′jȯr** *adj.* important or main

**Märs** *n.* the planet nearest Earth and the fourth from the sun

**maze** *n.* a confusing arrangement of paths

**Mer′cū·ry** *n.* the smallest known planet and the closest to the sun

**me·sa** (mā′sȧ) *n.* a flat-topped hill having steep sides

**Mi·guel Hi·dal·go y Cas·ti·lla** (mĭ·gel′ ĭ·däl′gō ē cäs·tï′yä) *n.* a leader in the Mexican fight for freedom from Spain

**Milk′y Way** *n.* the name of a group of stars that looks like milk spilled across the night sky

**Mï·nṵ′** *v.* a word in an African language for "I do not understand"

mis′un·der·stand′ *v.* to get the wrong idea about

moon *n.* the body in space that circles Earth and seems to be shining at night

Mount Âr′a·rat *n.* a mountain in eastern Turkey

mourn *v.* to show sorrow over a death or other loss

mourn′er *n.* a person saddened by a death

move·ment (mūv′ment) *n.* one part of a long musical work

mut′ter *v.* to speak in a low, hard-to-understand voice; to mumble

Nă′na *n.* a nickname for a grandmother

Na·va·jo (nä′va·hō′) *n.* an American Indian tribe of the southwestern United States

Nep′tune *n.* the eighth farthest planet from the sun

nes·tle (nes′sel) *v.* to cuddle up together

Ngu·yen Ho·a (nū′yen hō′a)

night′in·gale′ *n.* a kind of bird that sings its pleasant song mainly at night

nō′ble·men *n. pl.* people almost as important as kings and queens

north′ern lights *n. pl.* bright bands of lights in the sky sometimes seen from certain locations on Earth

ob′sta·cle *n.* an object that blocks the way

ode *n.* a poem that is meant to be sung

of·fi′cial *n.* a person who makes sure the rules of a game are followed

oil lamp *n.* a kind of light that uses liquid fuel

ōk′ra *n.* a shrub whose pods look a bit like green beans

out′house′ *n.* a toilet in a small shelter located outside a main building

out′skirts′ *n.* the edge of a town or city

o·ver·shoes (ō′ver·shūs′) *n. pl.* shoes worn over other shoes

Pä·dre·cï′tō

page *n.* a person who runs errands for an important person

Pä′pa·gō′ *n.* an American Indian tribe of the southwestern United States

pas′sage·way′ *n.* a path

Pe′pe

per′i·wiñ′kle *n.* a kind of flower with tiny, blue-purple or white blossoms

per·suade (per·swade′) *v.* to convince

**Phoe·nï′cian** *n.* a person who lived long ago near the eastern Mediterranean Sea—*adj.* belonging to the group of people who lived long ago near the eastern Mediterranean Sea

**Pï·cäs′sō** *n.* Pablo Picasso, a famous, modern, Spanish artist

**Pï′ma** *n.* an American Indian tribe of the southwestern United States

**plan′et** *n.* a large body of land in space circling the sun

**plead** *v.* to beg

**Plū′tō** *n.* the ninth farthest planet from the sun

**pomp** *n.* a grand, important appearance

**Ponce de León (pôn′se de le·ôn′)**

**Po·po·ca·te·petl (pō′pō·cä·tä′ pet·le)** *n.* a volcano in Mexico

**pop′py** *n.* a flower having simple, red blossoms

**port** *n.* a city where ships load or unload goods

**pot′ter·y** *n. pl.* objects made from hardened earth

**pov′er·ty** *n.* a way of living with very little money for food and shelter

**pranc′ing** *n.* the movement made when an animal springs from the hind legs

**pre′cious** *adj.* darling or adorable

**pro·ces′sion** *n.* a line of people moving forward slowly

**pros′pec·tor** *n.* a person who searches for oil or precious metal, such as gold, in the earth

**Puerto Rico (pwĕr′tō rï′cō)** *n.* an island in the Atlantic Ocean, south of the United States

**Quäng**

**Queen Ănne's lace** *n.* a wild flower having large clusters of tiny white blossoms

**rage** *n.* a very great anger

**ramp** *n.* a sloping path for getting between a high and a low place

**re′as·sure′** *v.* to comfort

**re′con·sid′er** *v.* to think things through again

**re·lā′tion** *n.* a person in the same family

**re·proach′ful·ly** *adv.* in an accusing way

**re·sist′** *v.* to keep yourself from doing what you want to do rė·spect′ *n.* a belief in the goodness of someone or something

rich *adj.* 1. having more than enough 2. full and pleasing to hear

roam *v.* to travel widely or to wander

role *n.* a part for an actor in a play or a singer in an opera

Rō·si′nä

Rō·si′tä *n.* a Spanish name meaning "little Rose"

rot *n.* a disease that destroys trees and fruit

rough (ruf) *adj.* plain or impolite

rub′bing *n.* the act of making a picture by moving a crayon back and forth on paper placed over an object such as a gravestone

salt′ cel·lar *n.* a small dish for serving salt

Sän′ti·ä′gō

sash *n.* a window frame and glass

Sat′urn *n.* a planet surrounded by bright rings, the sixth planet from our sun

schol′ar·ship′ *n.* a gift or prize of money to pay for school

scuf′fle *v.* to drag the feet while walking

scuf′fling *adj.* going or moving as in a hurried, confused way

scur′vy *adj.* nasty or awful

sė·cūre′ *adj.* free from worry and fear

Se·li′nä

shelf fuñ′gus *n.* a flat form of mushroom that grows on trees

shel′ter *n.* a place of protection

shrill *adj.* high and unpleasant in sound

shȳ *v.* to move so as to avoid something

skip′per *n.* the captain of a boat

slash′ing *adj.* moving with broad, rapid, sweeping strokes

slate *n.* a bluish-gray rock that is easy to mark

slave *n.* a person who is owned by, and works for, another

slug *n.* a kind of snail with no shell

sneer *v.* to speak in a way that shows dislike, often with a crooked smile

sō′lar sȳs′tem *n.* a sun and all the bodies in space that move around it

sol′id *adj.* steady or sure

sprout *v.* to begin to grow

squint *v.* to partly close the eyes

stain *n.* a coloring liquid that does not wash out

stal′lion *n.* a full-grown male horse

stär *n.* a body in space that gives off light (Stars appear to sparkle at night.)

**stĕr′ē·ȯ·scope′** *n.* an old-fashioned viewer for making flat pictures appear lifelike

**stern′ly** *adv.* without smiling; in a way that shows something is serious

**stock** *v.* to provide what is needed; to fill

**stout′ness** *adj.* meant for losing weight (*special meaning in this story*)

**sub′stance** *n.* a material that something is made of

**sug·ar-plum (shug′ar·plum)** *n.* a piece of candy covered with a smooth frosting

**sul′phur** *n.* a bright-yellow chemical (*Also spelled* **sulfur.**)

**sure (shur)** *adj.* steady

**sur·vey (sur·vā′)** *v.* to look over carefully

**sus·tain′ing** *adj.* helping to stand unpleasantness

**sym′pho·ny** *n.* a piece of music having several parts

**take the squâre root** (*or* **root**) *v.* to figure out a difficult mathematics problem (*special meaning in this story*)

**tal′ent·ed** *adj.* having the gift or ability to do something well

**teeth′ing** *v.* to grow teeth

**Pronunciation Key**

VOWELS: sat, hăve, āble, fäther, all, câre, ȧlone; yet, brĕad, mē, loadèd; it, practĭce, pīlot, machine; hot, nō, ôff, wagȯn; fo͝ot, fo͞od; oil, toy; count, town; up, ūse, trŭth, pull; mӯth, baby, crӯ, zephȳr.

CONSONANTS: cent, cider, cycle; c͟horus, c͟hute; ġem; light and though (silent), ghost; iñk; elephant; toe͟s; t͟hem; spec͟ial, mea͟sure, nation, nature.

**tend** *v.* 1. to watch so as to keep safe from harm 2. to take care of

**ter′mite** *n.* an insect that eats wood

**tĕr′race** *n.* a flat living area joined to, or on top of, a house

**this·tle (this′sėl)** *n.* a plant that has leaves covered with sharp points

**Tī′ä Rō′sä**

**time′out′** *n.* a resting time in a game

**Tí·o Juan (ti′ō whän)**

**tow′ėl-horse** *n.* a rack for hanging towels on

**trace** *n.* a sign that someone or something has once been in a place

**tran·sis′tȯr** *n.* a very small tube that provides power

**um′pire** *n.* a person who makes sure the rules of baseball are followed

**Ū·rā′nus** (*or* **ūr′ȧ·nus**) *n.* the seventh farthest planet from the sun

**urn** *n.* a large vase, often stone or metal

**Vē′nus** *n.* the second closest planet to the sun, between Earth and Mercury

**Vï′et·näm′** *n.* a country in Southeast Asia

**vi′ṣiȯn** *n.* a picture in the mind

**Vï′vä Mex·i·co (me′hï·cō)** *interj.* a Spanish cry that means "long live Mexico"

**von Karajan (von kär′ä·yän′)**

**Wä′shōe** *n.* the name of a chimpanzee who was taught to use American Sign Language

**wĕdged** *adj.* squeezed into a small space

**wick′ï·up′** *n.* an American Indian hut made of branches and bark

**width** *n.* the distance from one side to the other

**wōe** *n.* unhappiness or sadness

**wȯr′thy** *adj.* good enough

**wō′vėn** *adj.* made by criss-crossing two sets of threads over and under each other

**yam** *n.* a sweet potato or a vegetable like a sweet potato

**yoke** *n.* a wooden collar that joins work animals together